Our Family's First Year

A Helpful Guide and Journal

Mead Johnson
NUTRITIONALS

©1994, Mead Johnson & Company, Evansville, Indiana 47721 U.S.A. Published for Mead Johnson by Meredith Publishing Services, a division of Meredith Corporation, publishers of *Better Homes and Gardens*®, *Ladies' Home Journal*®, *Country Home*®, *Ladies' Home Journal*® *Parent's Digest*™ and *Traditional Home*®.

Dear New Parent:

Congratulations! Your baby is finally here. And as you begin adjusting as a family, Mead Johnson and the Enfamil® Family of Formulas will help you make that adjustment smoothly and with confidence.

Please accept this gift with our best wishes. Besides useful information, Our Family's First Year *provides a convenient way to record milestones. It also has room for busy parents to jot down their thoughts during baby's first year.*

We'd like to invite you, too, to join My Baby's Health Club (see page 9) and receive free newsletters with timely advice about caring for your baby plus valuable, money-saving offers.

Why do we do all this? Because at Mead Johnson, we're as concerned about your family as you are.

—Your friends at
Mead Johnson

contents

How to *use this book*

Each monthly chapter includes these features:

• **Timely Advice:** Read age-appropriate articles about baby's health, diet and development, plus changes you and your spouse are probably undergoing.

• **Space for Thoughts:** Month by month, jot down the changes you're seeing in your baby and other memories.

• **Room for Photos:** Maintain a month-by-month photographic journal of your baby.

• **Sticker Records:** Peel stickers from the front of the book to record special milestones.

• **Vital Statistics:** Keep a height-weight record plus information from doctor visits.

Always remember that babies develop at their own pace, and some perform an activity earlier or later than others.

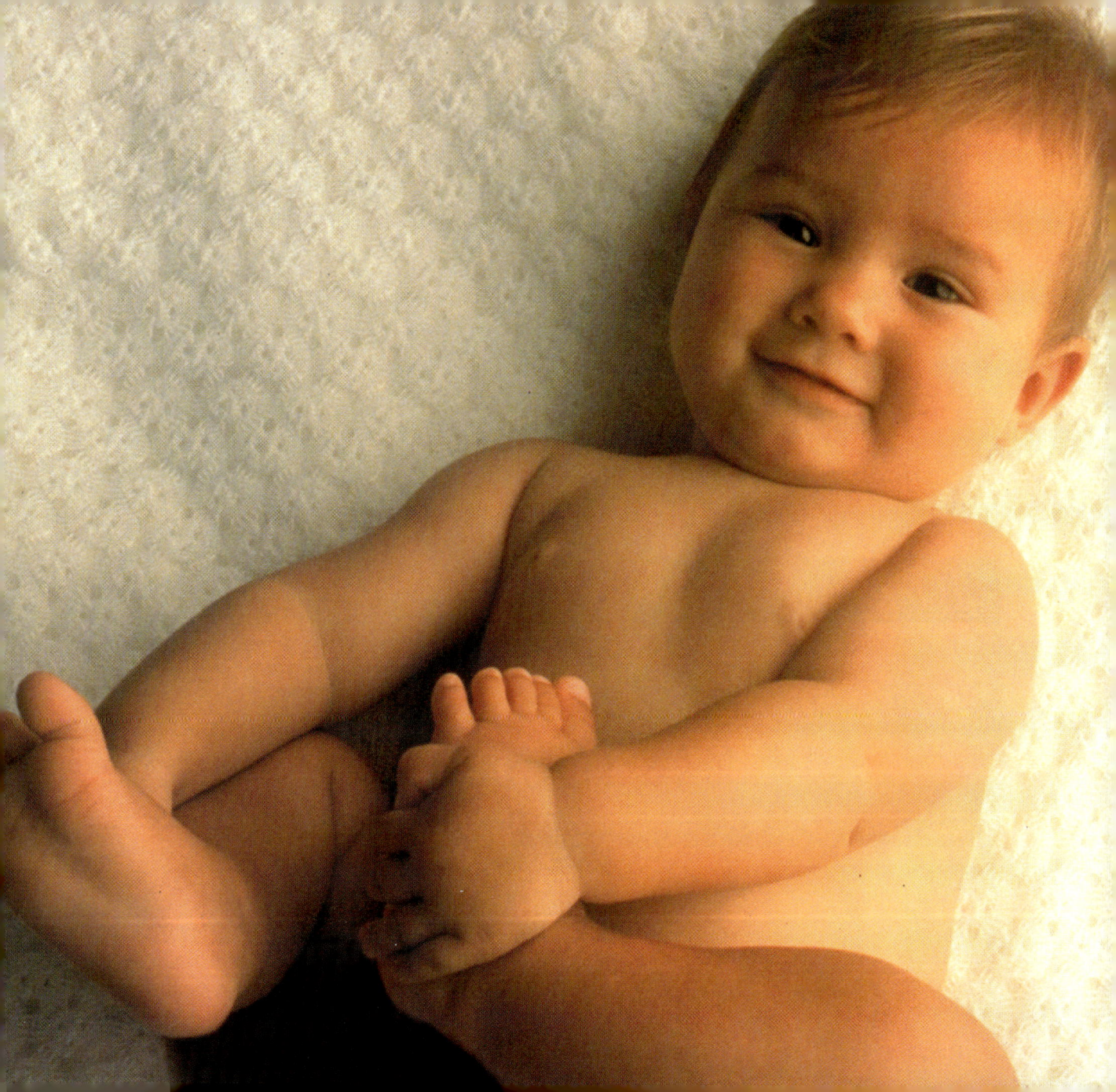

FIRST
DAY HOME

SLEEPS
ALL NIGHT

FIRST
SITTER

FIRST
TOOTH

SMILES

LAUGHS

COOS

IMITATES
SOUNDS

CLAPS HANDS

PLAYS
PAT-A-CAKE

PLAYS
PEEKABOO

WAVES BYE-BYE

FIRST
WORD

RECOGNIZES
MOTHER

RECOGNIZES
FATHER

TURNS HEAD

TURNS
TOWARD SOUND

HOLDS HEAD UP

DISCOVERS TOES

CREEPS

CRAWLS

REACHES
FOR OBJECTS

PLAYS WITH TOY

ROLLS FROM
TUMMY TO BACK

ROLLS FROM
BACK TO TUMMY

SITS ALONE

STANDS
WITH HELP

STANDS ALONE

FIRST
STEP

WALKS

CLIMBS
UP STAIRS

CLIMBS
DOWN STAIRS

FIRST
FORMULA

SECOND
FORMULA

HOLDS SPOON

EATS
WITH SPOON

FIRST
CEREAL

FIRST
VEGETABLE

FIRST
FRUIT

FIRST
MEAL

DRINKS
FROM CUP

SPECIAL
VISITOR

SPECIAL
VISITOR

SPECIAL
VISITOR

SPECIAL DAY

SPECIAL DAY

SPECIAL DAY

EVEN BABIES LIKE TO
HAVE CHOICES.

Like grown-ups, babies don't all like the same things. Some like formulas that closely resemble breast milk. Some are happier with formulas without lactose. And others would rather have something else altogether.

Which is why we created the Enfamil® Family of Formulas — Enfamil®, Lactofree®, ProSobee® and Nutramigen®. Of course, breastfeeding is the best choice. But when you prefer to use formula, you'll be able to choose one that's perfect for your baby's tiny digestive system. Even if it's a fussy one.

Each formula provides appropriate nutrition for your baby's first year and beyond. And when needs change, you can confidently switch to the right formula within the Enfamil Family. Our guide on the following page will help you to easily make the right choice.

After all, at Mead Johnson, health and nutrition have been our one and only focus for more than 80 years. And to us, making sure your little one gets the best possible care and nutrition is the biggest thing in the world.

Mead Johnson
NUTRITIONALS

OUR FAMILY IS PERFECT FOR YOUR FAMILY.

This guide was created to help you find the right formula for your infant's specific needs. If your baby has any of the problems listed below, consult your doctor to make sure they are feeding related. To use this chart, look over the "My Baby Has These Feeding Problems" section and match the feeding habits listed with your baby's characteristics. Once you've checked a box, follow the colored strip across to find the formula choice that could be right for your baby.

My Baby Has These Feeding Problems	*Which Could Mean*	*This Could Be The Formula That Fits*
☐ No ongoing problems interfering with feeding	An ability to easily digest and be nourished by a milk-based formula	**ENFAMIL®** • Milk-based • Has a blend of essential fats close to breast milk • Also available in low-iron formula (pink label)
☐ Common feeding problems such as: • Fussiness • Gas • Mild diarrhea	Trouble digesting lactose (milk sugar) No problem digesting milk protein	**LACTOFREE®** • Milk-based • Only brand that eliminates lactose, but keeps valuable milk protein • Looks, smells and tastes like milk-based formulas
☐ The possibility of allergies or milk sensitivity inherited from parents	An allergy to the cow's milk protein found in milk-based formulas -- or milk sensitivity	**PROSOBEE®** • Soy-based • Lactose-free • Eliminates milk protein • Contains easy-to-digest carbohydrate • Only major soy formula with no table sugar to avoid unnecessary sweetness
☐ Colic signs, such as: • Prolonged irritable crying for more than three hours each day ☐ Whole cow's milk protein allergy symptoms, such as: • Skin rash, sneezing, coughing, diarrhea, vomiting	Colic due to milk protein allergy (30% to 35% of colic cases are due to cow's milk allergies) An allergy to whole cow's milk protein	**NUTRAMIGEN®** • Hypoallergenic protein formula • Eliminates lactose (milk sugar) • Easy to digest

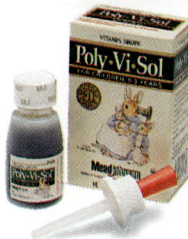

Mead Johnson
NUTRITIONALS

Consumer: Only one coupon is redeemable per purchase and only on specified product. You pay any sales tax.

Retailer: You are authorized to act as our agent and redeem this coupon at face value on specified product. We will reimburse you for the face value of the coupon plus 8¢ if submitted in compliance with Mead Johnson Nutritionals Coupon Redemption Policy, incorporated herein by reference. Send coupons to: Coupon Redemption Center, P.O. Box 870027, El Paso, TX 88587-0027. Cash value 1/20 of 1¢. Void where prohibited or restricted by law.

©Mead Johnson & Company, Evansville, IN 47721, USA

744017

744017

5 00087 00078 3

Mead Johnson
NUTRITIONALS

Consumer: Only one coupon is redeemable per purchase and only on specified product. You pay any sales tax.

Retailer: You are authorized to act as our agent and redeem this coupon at face value on specified product. We will reimburse you for the face value of the coupon plus 8¢ if submitted in compliance with Mead Johnson Nutritionals Coupon Redemption Policy, incorporated herein by reference. Send coupons to: Coupon Redemption Center, P.O. Box 870027, El Paso, TX 88587-0027. Cash value 1/20 of 1¢. Void where prohibited or restricted by law.

©Mead Johnson & Company, Evansville, IN 47721, USA

744017

744017

5 00087 00078 3

Mead Johnson
NUTRITIONALS

Consumer: Only one coupon is redeemable per purchase and only on specified product. You pay any sales tax.

Retailer: You are authorized to act as our agent and redeem this coupon at face value on specified product. We will reimburse you for the face value of the coupon plus 8¢ if submitted in compliance with Mead Johnson Nutritionals Coupon Redemption Policy, incorporated herein by reference. Send coupons to: Coupon Redemption Center, P.O. Box 870027, El Paso, TX 88587-0027. Cash value 1/20 of 1¢. Void where prohibited or restricted by law.

©Mead Johnson & Company, Evansville, IN 47721, USA

744488

744488

5 00087 50076 4

Mead Johnson
NUTRITIONALS

Consumer: Only one coupon is redeemable per purchase and only on specified product. You pay any sales tax.

Retailer: You are authorized to act as our agent and redeem this coupon at face value on specified product. We will reimburse you for the face value of the coupon plus 8¢ if submitted in compliance with Mead Johnson Nutritionals Coupon Redemption Policy, incorporated herein by reference. Send coupons to: Coupon Redemption Center, P.O. Box 870027, El Paso, TX 88587-0027. Cash value 1/20 of 1¢. Void where prohibited or restricted by law.

©Mead Johnson & Company, Evansville, IN 47721, USA

744470

744470

5 00087 60050 1

WE'LL WALK YOU THROUGH
EVERY STEP YOUR BABY TAKES.

So tiny. So precious. So full of questions. And, of course, you want the best possible answers. That's why we created a special club just to help families during that magical, but sometimes trying, first year.

It's called *My Baby's Health Club.* It's absolutely free. And it gives you help and advice. Money-saving offers. Why, there are even sweepstakes drawings.

Each month our newsletter, *Watch Me Grow,* gives you tips on health, nutrition and other information that are written specifically for the exact stage your baby is in.

A chance to win a layette.

During the month following your enrollment in *My Baby's Health Club*, you will be eligible for our Beatrix Potter™ sweepstakes*. Each sweepstakes winner will receive an enchanting Beatrix Potter layette worth $275, which includes: the "Storybook Collection," a five-piece crib set with sheets from Quiltex®, bumper pad, dust ruffle, quilt and a diaper bag. Each winner will also receive a musical Beatrix Potter mobile from Eden Toys and Wall Wonders removable Beatrix Potter wall decorations from Prelude Designs.

To join, call 1-800-472-1000 or fill out the attached card.

Once you join, you'll receive ongoing support that will help you be the best possible mom. Which will help you do the most important thing of all: Relax and enjoy your baby.

*No purchase necessary. Each entrant must be a mother expecting a baby or having an infant less than six months old, resident of the U.S. One entry per birth. Employees of Mead Johnson, its affiliates and agencies, and their families are ineligible. Each winner is required to sign an affidavit of eligibility and publicity release to permit the use of her name. Odds of winning depend on number of entries. List of winners' names available from Mead Johnson and published in My Baby's Health Club mailings to members.

The *new arrival*

What were we doing when we realized the time had come?

_____

_____

_____

_____

_____

_____

What do I want to someday tell my child about this time?

_____

_____

_____

_____

_____

_____

_____

What was my spouse feeling at the moment?

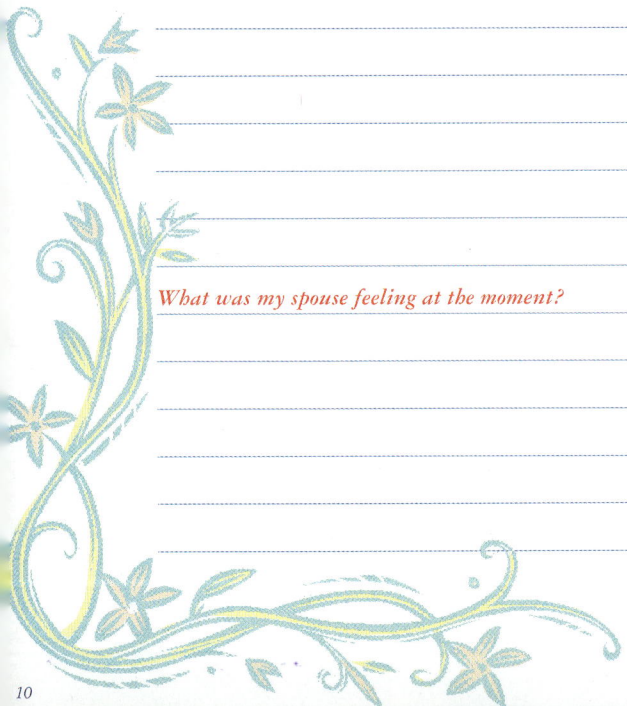

_____

_____

_____

_____

_____

Happy Birthday!

Name:

Time of Arrival:

Weight:

Length:

Color of Eyes:

Hair:

Doctor(s):

Favorite Nurse(s):

Hospital/Room No.:

Elizabeth Jordan		Great Grandfather		Great Grandmother		Great Grandfather
Great Grandmother						

Sarah V. Harris	Theodore Harris	Great Grandmother	Great Grandfather
Great Grandmother	*Great Grandfather*		

Patricia Pryor	William Pryor	Dorothy Johnson	
Grandmother	*Grandfather*	*Grandmother*	*Grandfather*

Yolanda S. Pryor	Marcus O. Johnson
Mother	*Father*

{affix photo here}

Baby's Name

Marcus Trevon Johnson

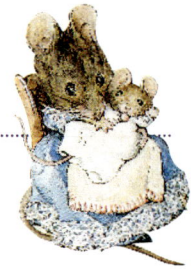

The baby's here, and you're on top of the world. But little questions are nagging at you: Why is your baby's head still so elongated? Why do you still look five months

The Baby's Here
What Now?

pregnant? The first few days after birth are exhilarating, but can also bring confusion. Here's a brief overview to help you through the immediate postpartum period.

THE BABY. She looks nothing like the smiling babies you see in commercials, but don't worry—she will soon. At birth, she is covered with vernix caseosa, the coating that protected her skin from the amniotic fluid. Her body also may be covered with downy hair that will disappear in the first weeks. Her head may be elongated from her trip down the birth canal. Her skin, particularly her hands and feet, may have a bluish cast.

MOM. Contrary to popular desire, you won't leave the hospital with a flat stomach. Your uterus is still enlarged and will take weeks to return to its pre-pregnant shape; the contractions you feel the first few days,

particularly if breastfeeding, will help it return to its original size. You may feel intense joy followed a few days later by a "low" feeling; this period of postpartum blues is related to hormones and likely will pass within the first few days or weeks.

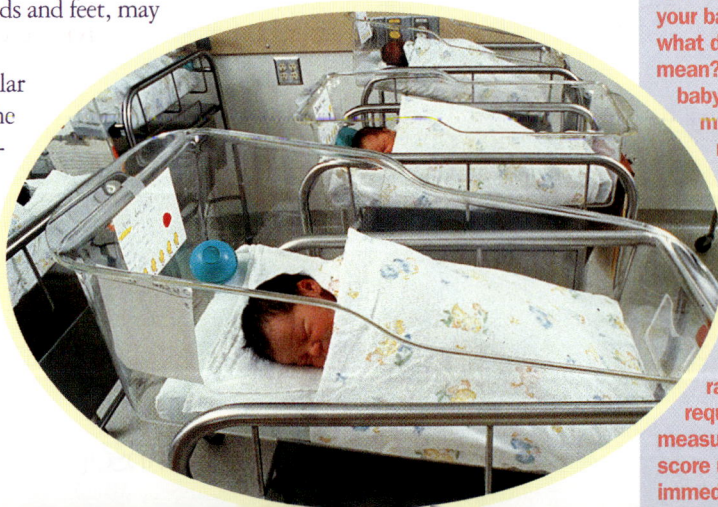

Baby's First Test

The nurse has just announced your baby's APGAR scores—what do those numbers really mean? The test assesses the baby's condition at one minute and again at five minutes after birth. The scores are based on observations made in five categories, and most babies rate a 7 to 10, which indicates good to excellent condition. Babies scoring 4 to 6 are rated "fair" and may require some resuscitative measures, and those who score under 4 usually require immediate lifesaving efforts.

What's That Stuff?

(on my baby's head)

The good news—it looks much worse than it really is. Cradle cap, a skin condition that affects the scalps of newborn babies, is as common as it is unsightly. In its mild form, it appears as greasy surface scales that flake when the baby's hair is combed. It usually responds well to a brisk massage with baby oil or petroleum jelly followed by a shampoo and several rinses to remove the oil and flakes.

In its more stubborn form, cradle cap appears as a yellow crustiness and produces heavy flakes. In this case, ask your doctor if a medicated shampoo is advisable. If so, make sure baby's eyes are protected when you rinse his hair.

Occasionally, cradle cap will worsen, recur or spread to the baby's face and neck. In these cases, doctors may recommend treatment with a topical cream.

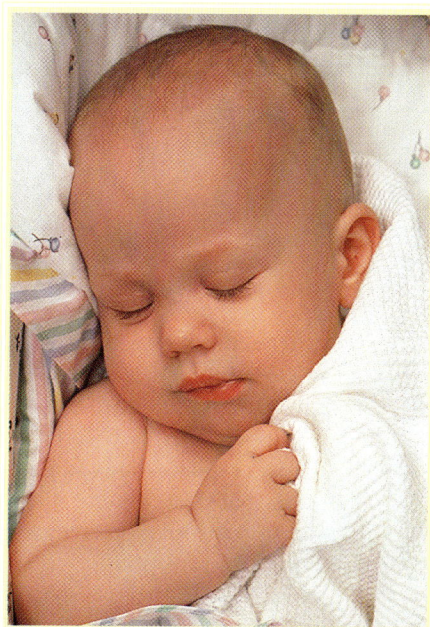

❀ *Don't be afraid to call your hospital nurses, day or night, with questions. When it comes to your baby, there's no such thing as a stupid question.*

Chris Johnson, newborn nurse and mother of three

What to Do Till the Cord Falls Off

Here are some tips to help you care for your baby's navel area while it is healing:

• Expose the area to air to hasten healing and enable the stump to wither and detach, usually within four weeks.
• Dab the area with a sterile cotton ball or gauze pad soaked in alcohol to speed drying.
• To lessen friction, fold your baby's diaper below the navel area, or use disposables with a special cut-out for the stump.
• Stick to sponge baths.
• Call the doctor if the site turns red or begins to ooze any type of discharge.

Jaundice— What You Should Know

You learned about jaundice, but are alarmed to now hear it's affecting your baby.

Relax—it's common and usually harmless. Characterized by a tanned, orangish or yellowish cast to the skin and the whites of the eyes, it occurs because the baby's liver—not yet fully functional—is unable to rid the blood of a substance called bilirubin.

Most jaundice doesn't require treatment, but close follow-up is necessary. If treatment is required, most doctors choose phototherapy—putting a baby under natural or artificial light to speed up the liver's removal of bilirubin. This therapy continues until the amount of bilirubin drops to and remains at a safe level.

13

1

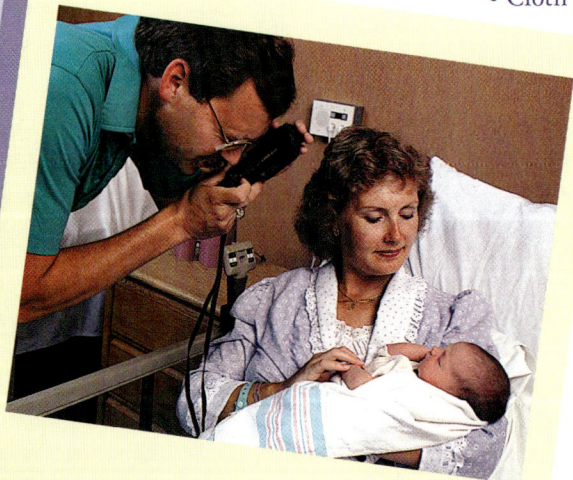

Baby's Progress

By the end of the first month, your baby may:

♥ **Be alert one out of every 10 hours**

♥ **Prefer patterns to solid blocks of color**

♥ **Make an "ahh" sound when Mom speaks or comes into view**

♥ **Startle, cry or quiet in response to loud or sudden noises**

♥ **Become calm when held upright and spoken to gently**

♥ **Focus easily on objects fewer than 8 inches from face**

Cloth or Disposable?

Deciding whether to use cloth or disposable diapers poses a problem: You want to do what's best for your baby, but also be environmentally responsible. Relax, the choice is yours—experts have concluded there is no "right" answer. Studies differ about which does less environmental damage. Disposables obviously fill up landfills, but cloth diapers create gallons and gallons of wastewater through washing. Other things to think about when choosing:

• Cloth diapers aren't as good as disposables at keeping moisture from baby's skin, and wetness is what causes rashes.

• Cloth diapers, since they must sit around before washing, tend to harbor bacteria, while disposables can be thrown out immediately.

• Cloth diapers require only washing and may be used again and again.

• Cloth diapers washed at home are considerably less expensive.

Picture *Perfect*

In the next few months, he'll smile his first smile, find his toes and learn to crawl. You'll want to keep some of those precious moments forever. Here are some tips to help you record the moment: ✳ Have the camera handy and keep it loaded. ✳ Choose fast-speed color film and use natural light from the outdoors as much as possible. ✳ For flash shots, use a slower film. ✳ Try to include other family members. ✳ Remember to date the pictures when you get them back and keep them in order in a family album.

NUTRITION *Your First Choice: Breastfeeding*

You want to give your new baby the best possible start, so you're considering breastfeeding. Experts agree breastfeeding has many benefits. Here's why:

• Breast milk, easily digested and packed with substances that protect babies against illness, contains most of the nutrients babies need for the first four to six months of life.

• Breastfeeding helps your uterus return to its normal size and helps you lose the weight gained during pregnancy.

• Breastfeeding creates a special feeling of closeness between you and your baby.

If this is your first experience with breastfeeding, be patient while you and baby get used to it.

To help ensure nursing success:

• Put your baby to your breast within a few hours of birth, if possible. The colostrum your breasts produce before your milk comes in is packed with nutrients and substances to protect your baby's health.

• Nurse whenever your baby is hungry. At first, your baby will nurse often—six to eight times every 24 hours.

• While your baby is learning to nurse, don't offer a bottle—even if it's only water.

• Ask an expert for advice. Many hospitals employ lactation consultants. Nurses and doctors can also provide guidance. Or, you can call your local La Leche League.

The Formula Choice

**If you've chosen to bottle-feed your new baby, rest assured that iron-fortified infant formula provides everything your baby needs for normal growth and development.
Enfamil ® is patterned after breast milk, so it's easy for most babies to digest. If your child has special feeding needs, your doctor may recommend *Lactofree* ®, a milk-based, lactose-free formula; *ProSobee* ®, a soy-based formula; or *Nutramigen* ®, which is made with protein that has been broken down.**

THE RIGHT START

Answers to Your Feeding Questions

Q: How often should I feed my new baby?
A: Most doctors recommend that newborns be fed on demand. In general, a breastfed baby will eat every two to three hours; a formula-fed baby usually goes three to four hours between feedings.

Q: How can I be sure my breastfed baby is getting enough to eat?
A: Many nursing mothers share this concern—especially before their babies' first weight checks. Here are a few ways to tell:

•Your baby nurses at least six times every 24 hours.
•You hear your baby swallow while nursing.
•Your breasts feel softer after nursing.
•Your baby wets at least six diapers every 24 hours.

Achieving Sibling Harmony

*S*ome of the closest relationships in the world can be between brothers and sisters. Siblings have the potential to love each other very deeply, and—with the help of sensitive parents—those feelings can start to develop as soon as the new baby comes home from the hospital.

It's especially important to consider your older child's feelings. Until now, he's received all the love from Mom and Dad. Once your newborn is home, be sure to give your other child time alone with you. To help foster a close relationship between your newborn and older child:

- Ask the older child to help you take care of the new baby. Give him special responsibilities.
- Understand your older child's jealousy. Listen to him when he talks.
- Give a toddler a "baby" of his own, such as a doll or stuffed toy, so he can mimic you.
- Reinforce an older child's role in the family to reassure importance. Tell him he is the older brother, not that he has a baby sister.
- Older kids may enjoy helping dress the baby or choosing what she will wear.
- Let your older child hold and cuddle the baby. Have the child sit down on a chair or cross-legged on the floor with the baby on his lap. Prop up the baby's head with pillows. If you bottle-feed, help an older sibling learn how.

Preparing for an Emergency

The quickest way to deal with an emergency is to prepare for it before it happens. Take a course either before or right after your baby is born to learn how to perform infant cardiopulmonary resuscitation (CPR), the Heimlich maneuver and minor first aid. The Red Cross, local hospitals and the YMCA or YWCA often offer classes. Also, keep insurance and medical information handy to grab quickly on the way out the door in case of emergency. Keep emergency numbers — hospital nurses, doctor's office, poison control center and others — next to the telephone.

❁ *I learned that colic isn't automatically to blame for every time the baby is fussy. I talked it over with my doctor, and we decided to test for other problems. Nothing else came up, so at least I knew what I was dealing with.*

Lisa Lavia Byrd, mother of two

When to
Call the Doctor

We've all seen television stereotypes of frantic new parents who call the pediatrician each time their baby sneezes. Admittedly, this is a little extreme, but babies can be confusing creatures, and unfortunately, they don't come with instruction booklets. Your pediatrician most likely does not consider new parents' questions bothersome, but here's a checklist to help you determine if you can deal with the situation on your own.

❀ Use common sense—but don't hesitate to call the doctor if you think something is wrong.

Chris Conyers, mother of one

TEMPERATURE. Although fevers often indicate conditions that are not particularly serious, most pediatricians like to be notified of any elevation of temperature in a young baby. If you suspect a fever, use a rectal thermometer to take her temperature. A rectal reading of 99.6 degrees is normal.

RESPIRATORY SYMPTOMS. Is your baby's breathing labored or raspy? Does she have a runny or stuffy nose? Is she coughing? If any of these symptoms are present, contact your doctor.

BEHAVIOR/SLEEP HABITS. Is your infant particularly cranky or inconsolable? Is she sleeping more than usual or less than usual, or is she difficult to rouse? Is her appetite normal? If any of these areas concern you, call.

DIGESTIVE SYSTEM. Is the baby vomiting, or has there been an unusual change in her bowel movements? Is she urinating normally? Any change might indicate a problem.

APPEARANCE. Does the baby look sick? Are her eyes sunken, dull or reddened? Is she pulling or digging at her ear? Any of these can indicate illness.

Ahhhhh *Choo!*

Besides Dad's nose, Mom's eyes and Grandma's grin, your baby inherits another trait: the potential for allergies. If one parent has allergies of any type, your baby has a good chance of developing an allergy of any type, too—up to 50 percent. If both parents have allergies, chances climb to 70 to 80 percent.

But babies aren't born with allergies—just the potential. And babies can't become allergic to what they don't come in contact with. In the first six months, the only allergy problems likely to arise will be food—newborns aren't often in contact with plants and animals. The most common allergies babies develop early are to milk and eggs. (See page 41 for advice on formula for allergy-prone babies.) More allergies may arise as baby becomes older and begins to try more foods.

Answers to Your Developmental Questions

Q: My mother insists that my 3-week-old only looks as though he's smiling because he's grimacing from gas pains. I say his smile is the real thing. Who's right?

A: It depends on the smile. If your baby uses his whole face, he's smiling from pleasure. But babies often go through a repertoire of faces, especially when they're asleep, and it could be these grimaces your mother is referring to. But even if your baby isn't smiling real smiles yet, he will be within the next few weeks. When it happens, reinforce it by smiling back, and he'll continue to dazzle you with toothless grins!

Q: My son seems to cry all the time. Even if he has a full stomach, a dry diaper and has had plenty of affection and contact, he still wails, particularly in the evenings. Our doctor says there's no physical cause. What are we doing wrong?

A: You did the right thing in checking with your physician to determine that the cause isn't physical. Your son's crying is probably due to colic. The latest research indicates colic is a result of the baby's development; it's no reflection on you or your parenting. The good news is that colic usually disappears during the first 12 weeks. Until then, try to remain calm and deal with your son's crying in as relaxed a fashion as possible. Ask your physician to suggest some "helpful hints" that may ease the tension, and see the suggestions on page 24.

Caring for the Circumcised or Uncircumcised Penis

If your son is circumcised, physicians recommend covering his penis with petroleum jelly and a clean gauze pad during each diaper change. During the healing, which usually takes 7-10 days, sponge baths are recommended; tub baths are more likely to expose the wound to bacteria. Once the wound is healed, and the umbilical cord has fallen off, cleanse the penis with mild soap and water during his bath.

No special care is needed for a newborn's uncircumcised penis. Use mild soap and water to cleanse it during his bath, as you do the rest of his body.

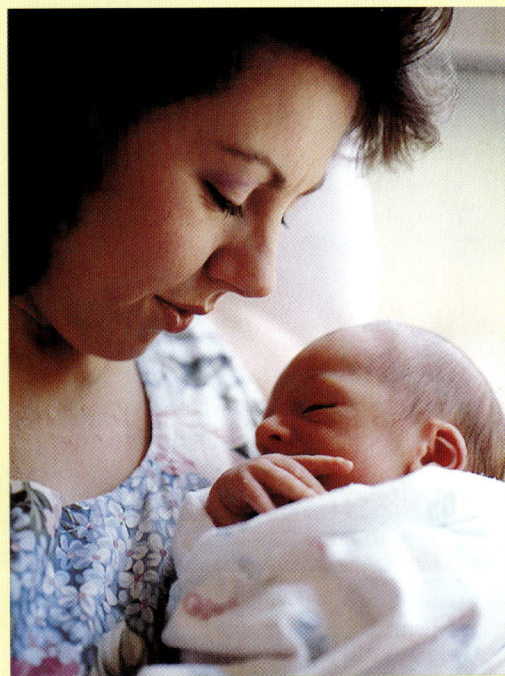

❀ *Relatives told us to quit picking up our baby every time he cried or we'd spoil him. But we decided at this age, his wants are his needs—and crying is the only way to express them. So we decided to trust our gut feeling.*

Jim Blume, father of two

thoughts

Does our baby resemble Mom, Dad, both or neither?

....

....

....

What has been the biggest change around the household?

....

....

....

Who are some of the visitors who have dropped by this past month?

....

....

....

What changes have I noticed in our baby since birth?

....

....

....

Am I taking time for myself?

....

....

....

{affix photos here}

milestones

Date

Details

Date

Details

Date

Details

Date

Details

Well-Baby Visit

Date

Length

Weight

Immunizations

Allergies or Sensitivities

Other Doctor Visits

Date

Reason

Date

Reason

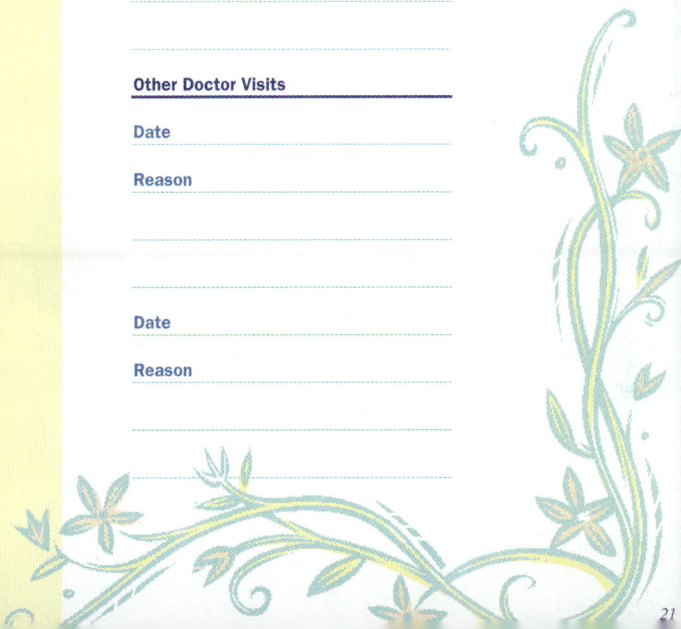

2

Baby's Progress

By the end of the second month, your baby may:

♥ **Smile in response to a smile**

♥ **Begin to track objects with eyes**

♥ **Lift head 45 degrees when lying on stomach**

♥ **Recognize breast or bottle and squirm eagerly for food when hungry**

♥ **Bat at toy with closed fist**

♥ **Keep head mostly upright when held in sitting position**

When Feeding Causes Problems

From time to time, every baby cries, spits up, has gas or has diarrhea. If your bottle-fed baby consistently exhibits any of these symptoms, consult your baby's doctor. Your doctor may suggest that you eliminate lactose with a formula like *Lactofree®*. If your doctor thinks your baby is sensitive to milk protein, a soy-based formula like *ProSobee®* may be the answer. If your baby's problem is colic, your doctor may recommend a special casein hydrolysate formula like *Nutramigen®*, made with protein that's been broken down into small pieces for easier digestion. For more information, see pages 23 and 35.

You're Never Too Old to Play
(and your baby is never too young)

For your baby, every experience is a learning experience—playtime included. Here are some rewarding play activities.

• Motion games, such as peekaboo, help your little one learn complex concepts.

• As your baby gets older, he will learn to mimic your voice and gestures. Your positive reactions will help your baby know he's doing things right.

• Dangle colorful objects—such as mobiles—above your baby's crib to help him learn to focus.

• Talk, sing and make up nonsense babble. Your baby will hear in your voice you are especially glad to be with him.

❋ *While your baby's lying on his back, move his legs as if he were pedaling a bicycle to the tune of "This Old Man" and other favorite songs.*

Anita Hauk, mother of four

NUTRITION

Formula-Making Made Easy

Good nutrition is vital for your baby's growth and development; so doctors recommend feeding breast milk or iron-fortified infant formula for the entire first year.

Parents who feed their babies *Enfamil®* can do so with confidence. It provides all the nutrients a baby needs and is designed to closely resemble breast milk. *Enfamil®* comes in powdered, concentrated liquid and ready-to-use forms. No mixing is needed for the ready-to-use *Enfamil®*, which comes in cans and handy, disposable *Nursette®* bottles. When preparing formula, remember these guidelines:

❥ Buy and use before the "use by" date on the container.

❥ Do not use a dented or damaged container.

❥ Before opening canned formula, shake cans and wash tops.

❥ Boil water for mixing concentrated liquid or powdered formula. Even when using bottled water, check the label to make sure the water has been sterilized.

❥ Measure accurately; prepare as directed.

❥ Shake bottle well before feeding.

❥ Refrigerate and tightly cover opened cans of concentrated liquid or ready-to-use formula. Use within 48 hours.

❥ Cover opened cans of powder with a plastic lid and store in a cool, dry place. Do not store in the refrigerator. Use within 30 days.

❥ Store prepared formula in the refrigerator for up to 48 hours.

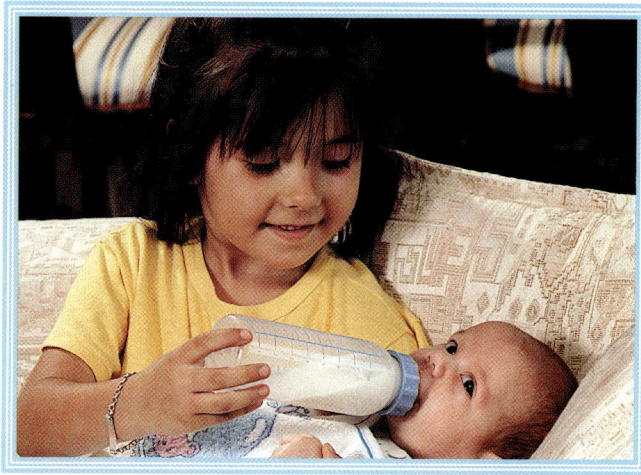

Burrrrrp!

For your baby, the end of a good meal is a good burp. It's necessary because air bubbles collect in baby's stomach and they could cause discomfort.

Burp your baby halfway through feeding and again at the end. Find a comfortable position: resting her over your shoulder; laying baby on her stomach across your lap; or sitting baby sideways on your lap, supporting her chest with one hand and rubbing her back with the other. Alternate rubbing and patting her back until you hear the distinctive "burrrp" sound. Cover your clothes with a small cloth in case baby spits up.

THE RIGHT START

Answers to Your Feeding Questions

Q: How much formula should I give my baby at each feeding?
A: Your doctor will suggest how much formula to offer your baby at each feeding, according to your baby's weight.

Q: I am unable to breastfeed my baby. Can my baby and I enjoy the same closeness that breastfeeding mothers and their babies feel?
A: The very act of feeding your baby, be it by breast or by bottle, provides the love and security your baby instinctively needs. The nurturing that accompanies each feeding helps create the emotional bonds between you and your baby that will last a lifetime.

Answers to Your Developmental Questions

Q: We're concerned about our daughter's muscle control. At 6 weeks, her head bobs from right to left and from front to back when we hold her in a sitting position.

A: Remember, a baby's head is the heaviest part of her body. Her neck muscles are not yet strong enough to hold it erect when she's held in a sitting position. That control will come within a few months.

Q: When our baby hears a loud noise, he arches his back, flings his arms and legs outward and starts to scream. Is this normal?

A: He is exhibiting the Moro reflex. When a young baby is startled, he reacts by arching his back, flinging his arms and wailing loudly. This reflex tends to disappear by the time the baby is 3 or 4 months old. To calm him, exert gentle, steady pressure on any part of his body.

Coping with Colic

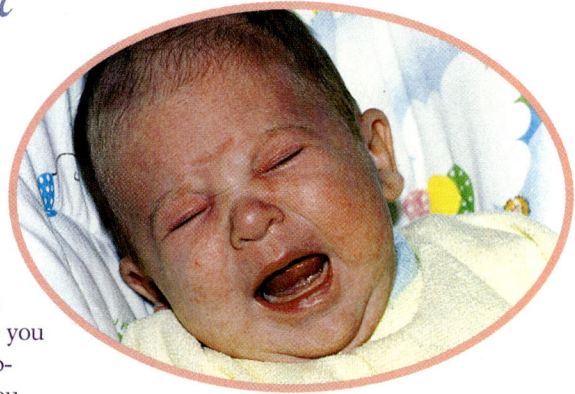

Just the mention of the word colic can bring fear to parents who have heard about the prolonged fits of crying that come with it. Once you have ruled out other problems, here are a few things you can try to pacify a fussy, colicky baby. Try one thing at a time, so when you find the magical way to soothe your baby, you'll know it.

🦶 Motion sometimes helps. Walk him, take him on a car ride or put him in a baby swing.

🦶 Try a pacifier, a quiet radio or rhythmic background noise such as a washing machine or fan.

🦶 Burp him more often.

🦶 Try swaddling him tightly to make him feel more secure.

🦶 Lay your baby across your lap and gently massage his back.

🦶 Try placing a hot water bottle full of warm water under his stomach.

CARING FOR AN IMMUNIZED BABY

Unfortunately, nothing you can do can prepare your baby for the sting of a vaccination at the doctor's office. Once home, though, watch for side effects—such as fever, soreness or swelling where the shot was given, fussiness, lack of appetite or drowsiness.

Symptoms usually go away in a day or two. Your baby's doctor may recommend *Tempra*® to reduce the fever and achiness, and it may be a good idea to give it to your baby before you leave the doctor's office.

Immunization Schedule:

	DTP	Polio	MMR	Hepatitis B ✱	Haemophilus	Tetanus - Diphtheria
Birth				✔		
1-2 months				✔		
2 months	✔	✔			✔	
4 months	✔	✔			✔	
6 months	✔				◆	
6-18 months				✔		
12-15 months					◆	
15 months			✔			
15-18 months	●	✔				
4-6 years	●	✔				
11-12 years				★		
14-16 years						✔

★ Except where public health authorities require otherwise.
◆ Depends on previous *Haemophilus infuenzae* type B vaccine given.
✱ Infants of mothers who tested seropositive for hepatitis B (HBsAg+) must receive hepatitis B immune globulin (HBIG) at or shortly after the first dose. These infants also will require a second hepatitis B vaccine dose at 1 month and a third hepatitis B vaccine injection at 6 months of age.
● For the fourth and fifth dose, the acellular (DTaP) pertussis vaccine may be substituted for the new DTP vaccine.

thoughts

Does our baby seem to be a good eater?

What is the biggest change I've noticed in our baby during the last month?

What have been my favorite songs to sing to our baby?

What is our baby's most cheerful time of the day?

What has been a typical sleep pattern?

{affix photos here}

milestones

Date

Details

Date

Details

Date

Details

Date

Details

Well-Baby Visit

Date

Length

Weight

Immunizations

Allergies or Sensitivities

Other Doctor Visits

Date

Reason

Date

Reason

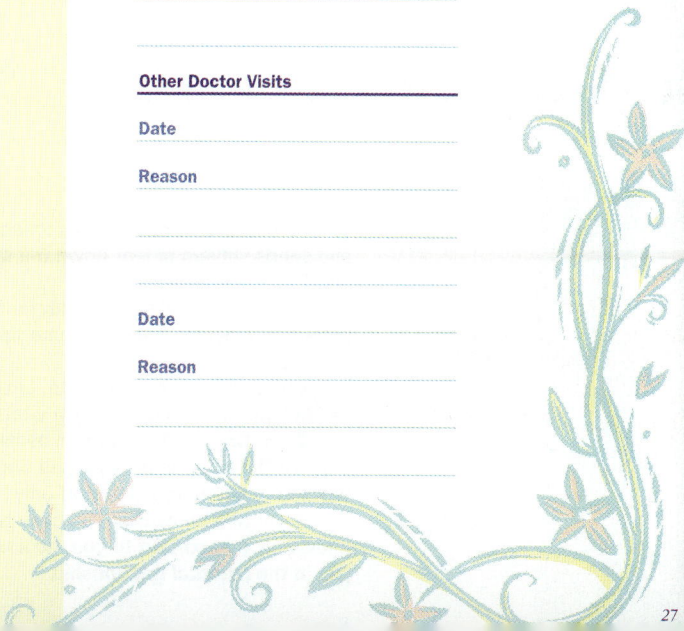

Baby's Third Month

Baby's Progress

By the end of the third month, your baby may:

♥ **Laugh and chuckle**

♥ **Lift head up to 90 degrees when lying on stomach**

♥ **Roll from stomach to back**

♥ **Attempt to reach for an object**

♥ **Grow visibly excited when a familiar person enters the room**

♥ **Stare for extended periods at hands or feet**

♥ **Raise chest when lying on stomach supported by arms**

If you work outside the home, finding a caring, safe environment is important to both your well-being and your baby's. Care falls into three basic types: a daycare center, a family home provider or a caregiver who comes into your home. Some general things you might ask: How many children will one individual care for? Are references provided? How are children disciplined? Here are some questions specific to each type of care:

• *Daycare center.* Are substitutes lined up?

Choosing the Right Caregiver

What about bringing sick children? Picking a child up late from time to time? Paying during vacation? What is the adult-to-child ratio?

• *Family home provider.* What's the maximum number of children on premises at a time? Can the provider suggest a back-up? Does anyone smoke in the house?

• *Nanny or in-home caregiver.* What experience have you had? Salary? Days off? What about staying late from time to time? Are you available weekends? Are you agreeable to light housekeeping? Cooking?

Dear Old Dad

What's short, weighs about as much as a bowling ball and sends shivers of fear down the spines of some men? Answer: a baby.

If your husband seems reluctant to jump into the parenting process, here are some tips to smooth the process:

➤ **First of all, communicate. Let Dad know his child needs him. Both parents play a vital role in baby's life.**

➤ **Let Dad be Dad—not an assistant Mom. Let him care for the baby on his own and encourage him to develop playtime routines that only he and baby share.**

➤ **Let him know that you need him now, too. If he knows he is important to you, he'll be more likely to join in the parental relationship.**

NUTRITION
On-the-Job Feeding

Answers to Your Feeding Questions

Returning to work outside the home doesn't mean you must abandon breastfeeding. Many mothers have successfully integrated breastfeeding into their work routine. Fortunately, it's fairly easy to keep your baby supplied with breast milk. You can express your milk by hand or with a pump into a sterile container while you're at work and deliver it to your caregiver to feed to your baby by bottle. You'll need to chill the milk in a refrigerator or an insulated container until you return home. Then you can store the milk up to 24 hours in the refrigerator or eight weeks in the freezer. Thaw the breast milk in the refrigerator and run the bottle under hot water to warm it up for baby.

If you are unable to express breast milk while you're at work, or simply choose not to, you can rely on supplementary formula. Patterned after breast milk, *Enfamil*® provides the nutrition your baby needs during the first year.

Smooth the transition by giving your baby at least a week to practice bottle-feeding before you go back to work. Introduce the bottle at a time when your baby isn't too hungry or too tired. Expect a little fussing; a rubber nipple isn't quite the same as a warm, soft breast.

✤ Use plastic bottle liners for freezing breast milk. One bag is just right for one serving — so you're thawing and heating the right amount.

Marilyn Hauk Essex, mother of one

Q: I'm returning to work soon. Can I use cow's milk to supplement my breast milk?
A: According to the American Academy of Pediatrics, iron-fortified formula is the only suitable substitute for breast milk in the first year. Cow's milk is difficult to digest and doesn't meet an infant's nutritional needs.

Q: May I add cereal to my baby's bottle to help her sleep through the night?
A: Your baby won't sleep any better if you give her cereal in her bedtime bottle. Doctors generally encourage parents to wait until a baby is 4 to 6 months old before introducing cereal.

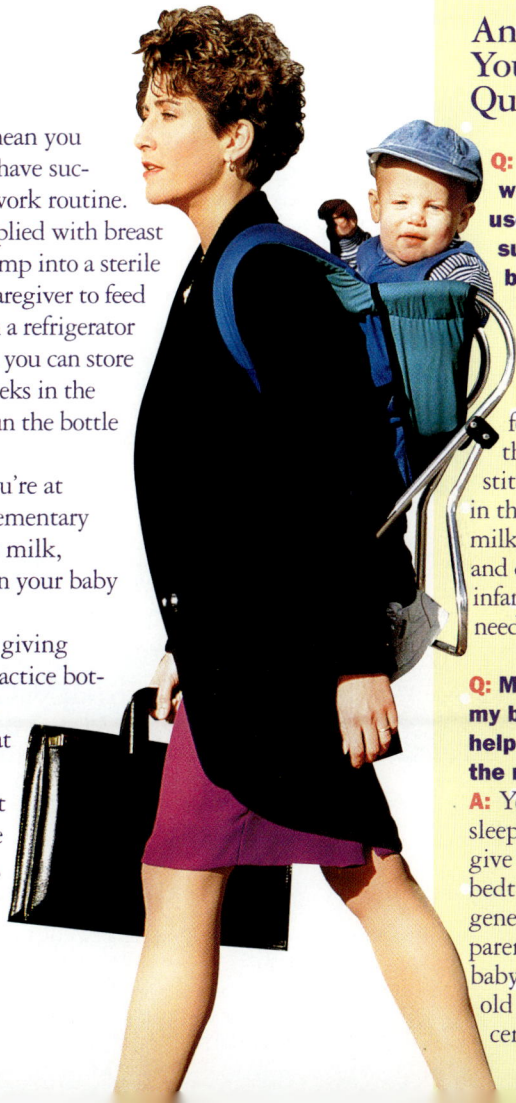

Answers to Your Developmental Questions

Q: My next-door neighbor says her baby will walk early because he bears his own weight when pulled to a standing position. My son doesn't do this. Will he be a late walker?

A: Weight-bearing at 3 months has no effect whatsoever on when a baby will walk. Many factors, possibly including heredity, determine when a baby will take off on two feet.

Q: When my baby is nursing, she'll pull away for brief periods and stop sucking. Feedings take forever. What's wrong?

A: At 3 months, a baby is becoming more aware of her environment. When a sibling squeals or someone on television makes a loud noise, the baby will stop feeding to check out the situation.

A Return to Intimacy

Returning to physical intimacy—the doctor may say "OK" while Mom's answer remains a resounding, "No way!" You usually can return to a sexual relationship within six weeks, at least physically. But many may not feel ready again for quite a while.

Moms may still be struggling with their physical recovery—plus long days and nights with the baby. Many men are ready to return to lovemaking soon after the baby is born; but some new fathers may subconsciously pull away from their partners, who are devoting most of their attention to the new baby. Your relationship *will* change after the baby, and being honest about your feelings with your partner and hearing your spouse's concerns can go a long way toward rekindling physical intimacy.

How to Maintain Your Own Nutritious Diet

Taking good care of yourself is just as important now as when you were pregnant. A nutritious diet is essential if you're going to keep up your energy as you gradually take off the weight you gained during pregnancy. If breastfeeding, you'll want to eat healthfully and drink plenty of liquids. Breastfeeding requires an additional 500 calories each day. But use the calories wisely. Some tips for helping you get the right stuff:

❖ Use the salad bar at your grocery store: stock up on cut-up vegetables for snacks.

❖ Stock up on low-fat yogurt for a tasty, nutritious pick-me-up.

❖ When cooking, double the recipe so you can store the leftovers in the freezer for a quick meal to pop into the microwave oven.

❖ Sprinkle raisins or other dried fruit on your cereal.

❖ Mix a tablespoon of dried milk in with your hot cereal or applesauce for an extra calcium boost.

thoughts

Has it been difficult to leave our child with a sitter?

How has caring for my own child made me appreciate my parents even more?

How have we adjusted household tasks to accommodate our new responsibility?

In what new ways do I appreciate my spouse?

What is the biggest change I've seen in our baby during the last month?

{affix photos here}

milestones

Date

Details

_____

_____

_____

Date

Details

_____

_____

_____

Date

Details

_____

_____

_____

Date

Details

_____

_____

_____

Well-Baby Visit

Date

Length

Weight

Immunizations

_____

Allergies or Sensitivities

_____

Other Doctor Visits

Date

Reason

_____

Date

Reason

_____

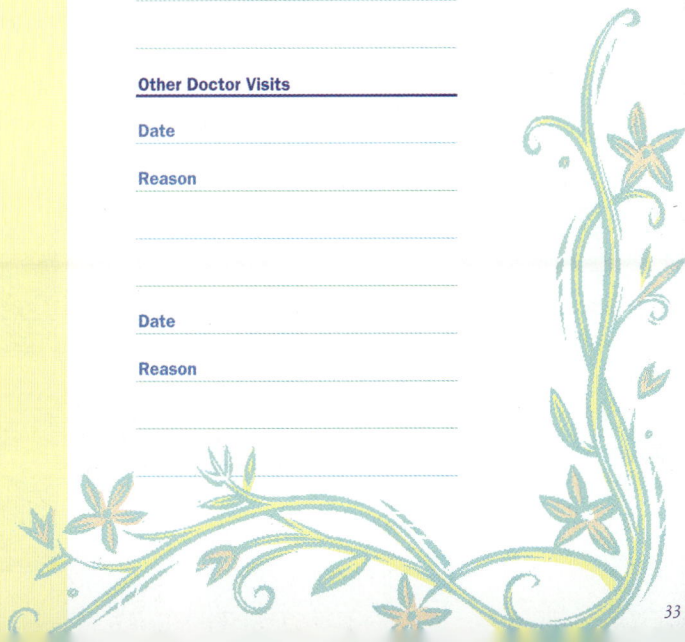

4

Baby's Progress

By the end of the fourth month, your baby may:

♥ **Babble, coo and squeal**

♥ **Shake a rattle**

♥ **Enjoy being pulled to sitting position**

♥ **Turn to stare at objects in all directions**

♥ **Examine objects with mouth, then hands**

♥ **Swipe at objects with open hand**

♥ **Be responsive up to an hour at a stretch**

Doctor, Doctor

You'll be seeing a lot of your baby's doctor during the first year. Many doctors schedule well-baby checkups at 2 to 4 weeks, 2 months, 4 months, 6 months, 9 months and 12 months. Here's how you can make the most of those visits:

• Write down questions as you think of them so you'll have a complete list when you go to the doctor's office.

• Take notes while you're there.

• Let your doctor know if you don't understand an explanation or an instruction.

Time Out for Fitness

You've changed three diapers, picked up toys and made dinner—and that's since you got home from work!

The last thing you probably want to do is head for the gym. But fitness *is* important. Exercising regularly relieves tension and gives you added energy. Taking baby along rather than hiring a sitter can make exercise feasible and may just make you closer.

Check out baby strollers designed to be taken on a jog. The manufacturer will probably offer a recommended age for your baby to begin using its equipment. Baby carriers that attach to the back of a bicycle also allow you to get outdoors and take along your little one. Make sure you dress your baby warmly—you will create quite a breeze as you pedal.

Answers to Your Developmental Questions

Q: My baby rolls all the way across the room. Is it time to childproof the house?
A: By all means, take a tour of your home and determine what areas could be hazardous to a mobile baby. It's never too early to be concerned about safety.

Q: I'm hearing such negative things about the reactions immunizations can cause. Should we discontinue them?
A: Please don't. The risk associated with immunization is very low. Your child has a much higher chance of being affected by one of the diseases prevented by shots than of suffering a serious reaction to a vaccine.

NUTRITION *Be Prepared When Diarrhea Strikes*

❀ Tie toys to the front bar of your baby's stroller so he doesn't toss them on the ground during an outing.

Joyce Rocha, mother of two

Even healthy babies suffer occasional bouts of diarrhea. When it happens to your baby, you'll want to be prepared. That's why it's wise to keep *Infalyte®*, an oral electrolyte solution, on hand.

When your baby passes watery, loose stools, you'll need to replace the lost fluids. Your doctor may recommend a product specifically formulated to prevent dehydration, such as *Infalyte®*.

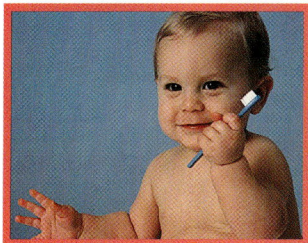

Don't give your baby liquids with high sugar contents, such as undiluted fruit juices or soft drinks. The sugar in these liquids may draw water out of your baby's body, making the diarrhea and dehydration worse. If diarrhea is a persistent problem, or if your baby consistently experiences gas and discomfort, your doctor may suggest that you eliminate lactose, the carbohydrate found in most milk-based products. Traditionally, doctors have recommended a switch from a milk-based formula to a milk-free soy formula to eliminate lactose.

Mead Johnson has a formula called *Lactofree®* that retains the milk protein while eliminating the lactose. If your baby still has problems and the doctor thinks the problem is with milk protein, a soy-based formula like *ProSobee®* could be the answer.

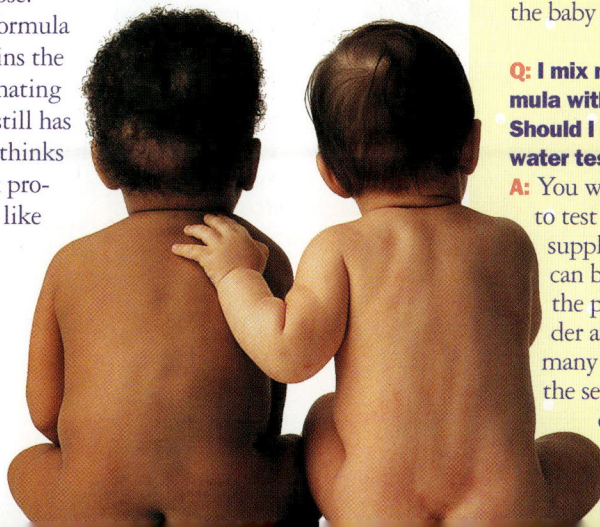

Remember the Fluoride

Even toothless babies need fluoride! The American Academy of Pediatrics recommends that breastfed babies and those using ready-to-use formula receive a prescription fluoride supplement such as *Poly-Vi-Flor®* in the first six months. Babies on formula made from liquid concentrate or powder should get extra fluoride if the level in the water is low or if bottled water is used.

THE RIGHT START
Answers to Your Feeding Questions

Q: How long can I keep a bottle of formula out of the refrigerator?
A: Formula is nutrient-rich, making it an ideal medium for bacteria growth. Prepared formula should be used or discarded within two hours of mixing or removal from the refrigerator. Feedings should be completed within one hour from the time the baby starts to drink.

Q: I mix my baby's formula with tap water. Should I have the water tested for lead?
A: You would be wise to test your water supply for lead. It can be found in the pipes, pipe solder and faucets of many homes, and the service lines of older homes.

Longing for Routine

Experts agree that it takes three to six months for a baby to develop a proper sleep cycle, so now might be a good time to help yours learn a healthy sleep routine. Some tips toward that goal:

✶ A newborn can learn what are daytime and nighttime activities.

Don't play with your baby when he wakes you at 3 a.m. and won't go back to sleep. Give the message that nighttime is for sleeping.

✶ Try to develop a nighttime ritual that signals your baby when it's bedtime. When baby becomes drowsy, read him a book, rock him or give him a quiet bath. Then say a loving good night and leave the room. Be consistent with the ritual so baby will know this is a routine he can depend on.

✶ Start putting your baby to bed while he is drowsy, but not asleep. This will teach him to fall asleep on his own.

✶ Don't leave the bottle in the crib. New teeth are damaged by sugars in milk and juice if they stay in baby's mouth. And if he must have a bottle to fall asleep, he'll want one in the middle of the night if he wakes.

Baby Grins

By now, you've probably seen it—that special smile your little one has only for you. You may even have heard her giggle as you tickled her tummy or lifted her into the air. If you relish those baby smiles and giggle along with her, your baby will develop that humor into a fun-loving attitude. The easiest way to make your child laugh is to laugh yourself. Make funny faces, sing high-pitched songs, tickle your baby. If your mood is joyful, your child's likely will be too. Bright toys with patterns also bring good-natured grins. Go for the regular kiddie games—silly sessions of peekaboo and pat-a-cake will delight your little one.

How to Answer Your Baby's Cries

It's 2 in the morning, and you wake from a sound sleep. The baby's crying—again.

Is he hungry? Wet? Lonely? With some careful listening, the *way* he's crying can give you a clue. The most startling type of cry is a piercing, painful-sounding alarm that occurs when the baby is experiencing discomfort, which can signal anything from stomach cramps to an errant diaper pin. The second-most-urgent type of cry is the demanding one that indicates hunger; it is quickly and easily satisfied with breast milk or formula. The boredom cry, a hollow-sounding, "come-and-get-me" cry, is used to communicate loneliness; it usually ceases when the baby is picked up. A rhythmic, non-urgent, exhausted-sounding cry indicates fatigue or overstimulation.

✶ Remember—most babies wake up in the night. Talk softly and rub him gently, but refrain from picking him up.

✶ There are bound to be some tiring nights as you get your baby into a sleep schedule. Keep at it—it will pay off as he gets older.

thoughts

What is the biggest change I've seen in our baby during the last month?

What things am I adding back to my routine that were put on hold immediately after birth?

What gave me the biggest laugh during the last month?

How have I streamlined the process of bundling up our baby for travel?

What special joy has our baby given us this last month?

{affix photos here}

milestones

Date

Details

Date

Details

Date

Details

Date

Details

Well-Baby Visit

Date

Length

Weight

Immunizations

Allergies or Sensitivities

Other Doctor Visits

Date

Reason

Date

Reason

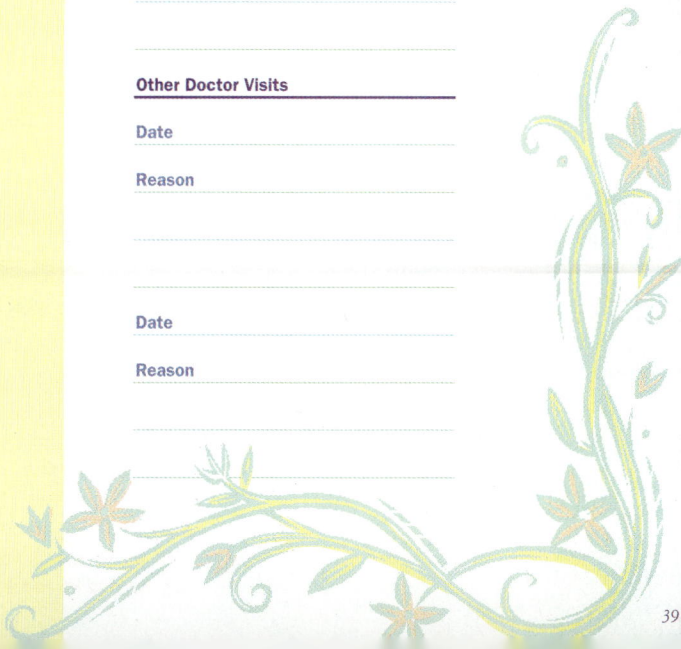

5

Baby's Progress

By the end of the fifth month, your baby may:

♥ **Be alert for 90 minutes to two hours at a time**

♥ **Turn head deliberately to follow sound or object**

♥ **Lean over or look around obstacle to search for fallen object**

♥ **Do modified push-ups and make swimming motions with arms and legs**

♥ **Roll from stomach to back and back to stomach**

Making Time for the Two of You

Who says you have to go out to have a romantic evening together?

With a little planning and willingness for flexibility, you and your spouse can steal away a few hours of time, while your baby sleeps peacefully in a nearby room. By now your baby may be sleeping through the night and has some sort of predictable feeding schedule. Work around this schedule to plan your romantic meal. Set the table with your prettiest dishes and order takeout from your favorite restaurant. Let them know when you'd like it ready so you or your spouse can pick it up at a convenient time. When your baby's sleeping soundly, sit down to a peaceful meal together, complete with candlelight.

Getting a Very Early Start on Reading

Reading enthusiasm is one of the most important gifts you can give your child. The best way to encourage that enthusiasm: Read to your baby regularly, from now right up to the time he may prefer to read to you.

Answers to Your Developmental Questions

Q: **My daughter seems to put everything in her mouth. Is this OK?**
A: It's perfectly normal. Babies explore their world first with their mouths, then with their hands. But try to keep her from putting objects in her mouth that have germs or could injure her by choking or cutting.

Q: **All of a sudden, my son won't have anything to do with our neighbor, who has visited frequently since the baby was born. Why?**
A: You may be dealing with the beginnings of "stranger anxiety." Your baby is aware enough of his loved ones to perceive anyone else as threatening. Don't force him to interact, but allow him to see you visiting and enjoying the guest's company.

NUTRITION *Introducing Solid Foods*

❀ When your baby's learning to eat solids, spread lots of newspapers under her chair to catch the mess.

Jan Richardson, mother of four

What's the best time for introducing your baby to solid foods? When she's ready! Doctors usually recommend introducing solid foods between 4 and 6 months. Babies who are ready have good head control and will lean forward and open their mouths when a spoonful is offered. There's no reason to rush solids. If a baby repeatedly pushes the food out of her mouth, she may not be ready. Wait a week and try again. Your doctor will probably suggest a single-grain cereal, like rice fortified with iron, for your baby's first food. Of all the grains, rice is most commonly recommended. One or two teaspoons of cereal is enough to get started. Offer the cereal in a small spoon, and be prepared for a mess!

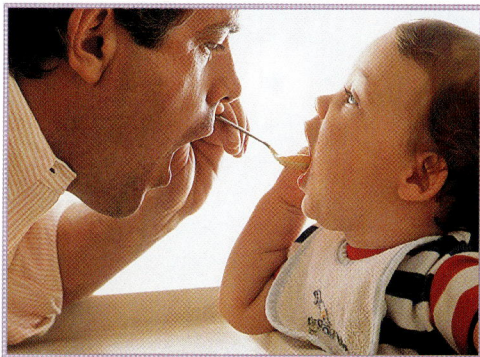

When you begin feeding solid foods, give them to your baby once or twice a day. Before each feeding, give your baby just enough breast milk or formula to take the edge off his hunger.

After cereal, the foods you'll introduce include: fruits, vegetables, fruit juices and meats. Ask your doctor before introducing egg yolks. Introduce one new food at a time, waiting about a week until you see how each food agrees with your baby before adding something else to his diet.

Throughout most of baby's first year, solids should take second place to either breast milk or iron-fortified formula.

Is Your Home Baby-Proof?

Your baby is becoming more mobile, so make sure your entire home is baby-proof.

✔ Install safety gates at the top and bottom of all stairways. ✔ Cover all electrical outlets, and move electrical cords out of reach. ✔ Keep small objects off the floor. ✔ Attach safety latches on all cabinets and drawers.

THE RIGHT START

Answers to Your Feeding Questions

Q: I'm worried my baby has inherited allergies. What type of formula should I use when I wean my baby?

A: Your baby's doctor may recommend a formula that has no cow's milk protein, like *ProSobee®*, and that you supplement the formula with breast milk. Breast milk contains antibodies that can protect your baby from allergies. Ask your baby's doctor how often to breastfeed as you make the switch.

Q: How can I be sure the formula I feed my baby is fresh?

A: Mead Johnson formulas are dated to ensure the nutrient levels and quality of each product are at their peak. Check the date imprinted on the top or bottom of a Mead Johnson formula container.

{affix photo here}

thoughts

What feeding changes have I introduced this last month?

_____

What is the biggest change I've seen in our baby during the last month?

_____

How have I managed to make time for my spouse during the last month?

_____

milestones

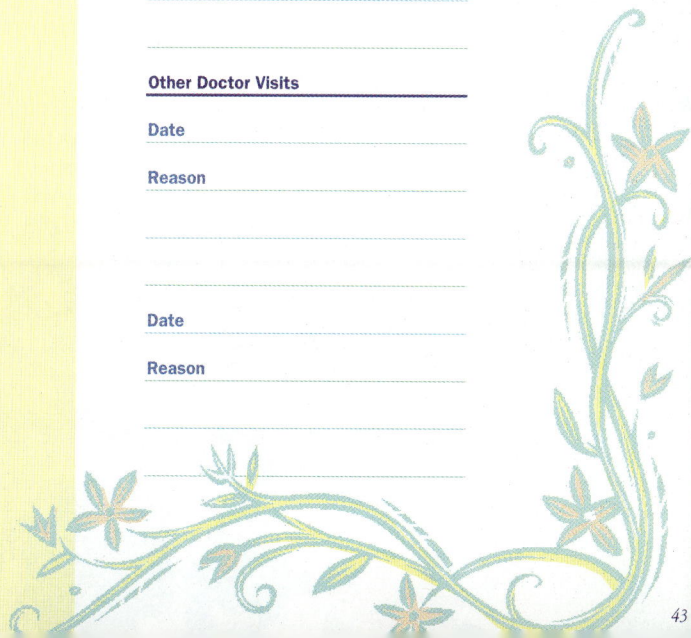

Date

Details

Date

Details

Date

Details

Date

Details

Well-Baby Visit

Date

Length

Weight

Immunizations

Allergies or Sensitivities

Other Doctor Visits

Date

Reason

Date

Reason

6

Baby's Progress

By the end of the sixth month, your baby may:

♥ **Sit independently**

♥ **Push up on hands and knees and rock back and forth**

♥ **Hold own bottle**

♥ **Pass objects from hand to hand**

♥ **Support most of own weight when held in standing position**

♥ **Like to look at objects upside-down to create change in perspective**

Baby Talk

"Ooh, dere's my itty bitty pwitty wittle girl."

"Hello, Rebecca, how are you?"

It's hard to resist. Infants seem to lend themselves to the high-pitched, sing-song way of speaking identified as "baby talk." "Hello, Rebecca, how are you?" just doesn't seem as perfect a greeting as "Ooh, dere's my itty bitty pwitty wittle girl." But studies have shown that baby talk, while endearing, does nothing to enhance verbal skills—and might even be a hindrance. While saying "dolly" for "doll" is harmless and naturally more appealing, words such as "baba" for "bottle" and "wawa" for "water" only confuse the child's budding language development. Socially, baby talk puts the child at a disadvantage. Who wants their 5-year-old asking to be excused from kindergarten to "go make a tinkle in the potty?"

Play-Group Possibilities

Meeting regularly with other parents and babies can be fun and rewarding. Many churches and synagogues will let you use a nursery room during the week. To find participants, make a flyer with your name, your children's ages and the time you'd like to meet, then distribute it in your neighborhood, church, synagogue or YMCA. If the response is overwhelming, limit the group size to the first six to eight who showed interest, then start a waiting list.

Answers to Your Developmental Questions

Q: Now that my baby is sitting independently, does he still need his special seat in the bathtub?

A: Don't be in too big a hurry to take him out, unless the seat is bothering him. He may feel secure sitting on dry land, but water is different. The important thing to remember is that he shouldn't be left alone in the tub—bath seat or no bath seat—for even an instant.

Q: My daughter fusses in her car seat, which faces the rear. Is it time to move her into a forward-facing seat?

A: Probably. The instructions included with your seat should say how much weight it safely holds—many allow weights of only up to 18 or 20 pounds. So perhaps it is time to switch to a different seat because of safety reasons.

44

NUTRITION *Bedtime Bottle Blues*

Here's one word of advice for parents tempted to give their babies bottles when putting them down at bedtime or naptime: Don't! This practice, according to the American Dental Association, can lead to baby-bottle tooth decay. During sleep, the natural cleansing action of saliva in the mouth tapers off. That means the formula your baby drinks just before drifting off to sleep remains in contact with the teeth for a long time. The lactose

or other sugar in the formula promotes the growth of bacteria that cause tooth decay. And formula isn't the only culprit: Breast milk, cow's milk and fruit juice all contain sugars that can cause

tooth decay. Also, from a behavioral standpoint, your baby needs to learn how to put himself to sleep without a bottle. Here's one way to do it: Give your baby his normal bedtime feeding. When he starts to look drowsy, stop the feeding and put him in his crib. If necessary, soothe your baby by rubbing his back or tummy or by singing a song. This may be a good time to establish a regular bedtime routine.

Although an occasional bedtime bottle won't harm your baby, it's best to "just say no." Repeated bedtime bottles may turn into a habit that takes several years to break. If your baby insists on taking a bottle to bed, try giving him a bottle filled with water.

Oh, the PAIN of it all!

If teething is making your baby uncomfortable, try rubbing his gums with a clean finger. Or, give your baby a cold teething ring to chew on. Medicine that you rub on your baby's gums may soothe your baby temporarily—until saliva washes the medicine away. Pediatric pain relievers that contain acetaminophen, such as *Tempra®* drops, may provide relief. Ask your baby's doctor about an appropriate dose.

Answers to Your Feeding Questions

Q: My chubby baby is incredibly cute. However, I'm worried he is too fat. Is there anything I can do to help him slim down?
A: If you think your baby is gaining too much weight, consult your baby's doctor. Diet restrictions may compromise a baby's growth and development.

Q: My baby is drinking more formula and I want to buy it as economically as possible. What are the least expensive forms of *Enfamil®*?
A: Concentrated liquid formula and powdered formula usually are the best buys. But compare prices in your local stores to determine what form and price best meet your needs.

What About Walkers?

Baby walkers have been marketed as a fun method for developing motor skills. But the American Academy of Pediatrics advises parents to avoid them because of potential danger. Each year, more than 25,000 infants are treated in emergency rooms because of baby walker injuries. Half of these are caused by falls down stairs while the baby is still in the walker. And some babies in walkers have been scalded when they pull down pots from the stove. Some experts approve of walkers for limited periods—if baby is carefully watched and well away from inclines or stairs.

Have Baby Will Travel!

Preparation is the key to traveling with a baby. Whether you're going by plane, train or automobile, keep these tips in mind as you plan and pack:

• Keep your diaper bag handy, organized and well-stocked. Store some entertaining toys and plenty of wipes, diapers and at least one change of clothes. Pack a plastic bag for storing soiled clothes.

• Avoid hunger cries. If you're bottle-feeding, pack enough formula, bottles and nipples to accommodate delays.

• Don't forget a favorite blanket or stuffed animal.

• Let your booking agent know you'll be traveling with an infant. On board, ask an attendant to warm formula or baby food.

• Make sure the hotel has a crib reserved for you.

WEIGHING YOUR WORK OPTIONS

Juggling your career, your baby and your marriage isn't easy—yet many mothers are doing it. Here are some strategies:

➥ If possible, ease back into work. See if your employer would be willing to let you work shorter days for your first few weeks back. Consider job sharing or working part-time.

➥ Delegate chores. No one can do it all, so why not let someone else do the things you like least? Send the shirts to the cleaners and hire a high school student to clean your house, mow the lawn or shovel snow.

➥ Take microvacations. Some companies allow you to break up your vacation days into hours. Take an afternoon off to rest.

➥ Start your own at-home business. If you have a skill you can market, you may be able to work at home. But don't quit your day job—yet. Hold onto your current position until you are making enough at home to sustain your lifestyle.

To Work or Not to Work?

You may have already spent a great deal of time pondering this point. The only one who knows the best choice for your family is you. Will your baby be better off if you stay home? If you do decide to stay home, will you wish you were at work instead? Your child can sense your happiness and well-being: If you're happy, your baby will be, too.

thoughts

Has our baby experienced teething pain? What helped?

How have my feelings toward work outside the home changed?

What is the biggest surprise our baby has given me this month?

What have I done to make my home safe for our baby?

What is the biggest change I've seen in our baby during the last month?

{affix photos here}

milestones

Date

Details

Date

Details

Date

Details

Date

Details

Well-Baby Visit

Date

Length

Weight

Immunizations

Allergies or Sensitivities

Other Doctor Visits

Date

Reason

Date

Reason

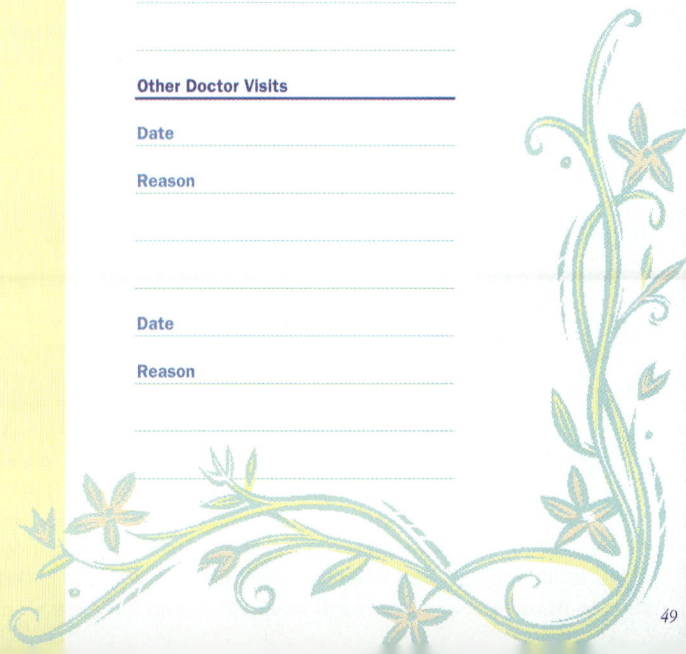

7

Baby's Seventh Month

FEAR CREEPS IN

Baby's Progress

By the end of the seventh month, your baby may:

♥ **Show interest in attempting to crawl**

♥ **Demonstrate marked increase in attention span**

♥ **Enjoy banging and shaking objects**

♥ **Associate picture of baby with own image**

♥ **Stand with support**

♥ **Change easily from a sitting to a crawling or creeping position**

By 7 or 8 months, baby's ability to recognize familiar faces brings her great pleasure—and, conversely, being confronted with a stranger's face causes distress. Your child eventually will learn that people other than Mom and Dad—like a new babysitter—are OK, and that Mom and Dad always return. But here are a few ways you can ease the pain now:

• Cultivate a special soft toy or blanket. When you're away, it may be reassuring to know that at least one special "friend" is near.

• Let your baby check out the new faces. Have others approach your baby quietly, talking to you first, before turning their attention to her.

• Reassure your baby that you will be back, then leave quickly.

Balancing Work and Home

The endless demands of family and home are complicated, and at times, exhausting. Here are some tips to help you keep a good outlook and attitude: ▲ Organize your day. If morning is your nemesis, pack your baby's bag and fill his bottles the night before. If dinnertime increases your stress level, stock your freezer with heat-and-serve meals. ▲ Prioritize your tasks. At the beginning of each month, mark all of the family's events and activities on one calendar. Allow time for bill-paying, balancing the checkbook, exercising, housecleaning, a night out with your spouse and a luncheon with your friends. Say no when people ask you to take on additional commitments.

▲ Share the responsibility. Sit down with your spouse and discuss ways you can divide chores equitably or figure out a way you can afford to hire out some of the work. You also may need to lower expectations. It is better to skip making the bed than to become too tired and irritable to give your baby the kind of nurturing he deserves.

THE RIGHT START

Answers to Your Developmental Questions

Q: When my husband and I try to have a conversation, our daughter shrieks and squeals at the top of her lungs until she has our full attention. Do we have a problem?

A: No. Your daughter is showing a desire to be included in social interaction, which proves she's acclimating nicely to her world.

Q: My son seems to get excited when he sees a picture of a baby on TV or in a magazine. Does he know he's a baby?

A: Apparently so. Even very young babies seem to be attracted to the faces of children more than to those of adults. You might want to increase his enjoyment by making a homemade book of baby faces or by showing him pictures of himself in the family album.

NUTRITION *Positive Feeding*

❀ *Put a water filled teething ring in the freezer to offer your baby for teething pain.*

Lois White, mother of two

Babies have a way of letting you know how they feel about their food. If they don't like a particular food, they won't hesitate to spit it out. When this happens—and it will if it hasn't already—stay calm. Try to remember that you can't always control what your baby eats. What you can control is your attitude. And it's your attitude about food that ultimately will shape your baby's eating patterns for the rest of his life. Here's how to make eating a positive experience:

• Respect your baby's food preferences. If your baby refuses to eat a new food, don't make an issue of it.

• You can increase the likelihood your baby will accept a new food by serving it at the beginning of a meal.

• Let your child decide how much is enough. He will tell you when he's full by turning his head away from his food, playing with his food or becoming restless.

• Instead of comforting a crying baby with food, try to find out what he wants. He could be asking for someone to hold him or change his diaper.

• As your baby gets older, avoid using food for a reward.

Raising a **Vegetarian**

At first, vegetarian diets pose few problems for babies. They get most of the nutrients they need from breast milk (assuming their mothers are well-nourished) or iron-fortified infant formula. As babies grow, and get more of their nutrition from solid food, their menus require special care to ensure an adequate supply of high-quality protein and other nutrients. If you're considering a vegetarian diet for your baby, talk to his doctor about food selection and a vitamin-mineral supplement.

Answers to Your Feeding Questions

Q: My daughter isn't very enthusiastic about eating solid foods. How can I encourage her?
A: Let your daughter take her time getting used to solid foods, as long as she is consuming adequate amounts of iron-fortified formula or breast milk. But be sure that your daughter hasn't consumed so much breast milk or formula that she isn't hungry.

Q: We're planning a trip. What is the best way to carry my baby's formula?
A: Keep bottles filled with prepared formula chilled in an insulated container with ice. For longer trips, pack additional cans of concentrated liquid or powdered formula. For convenience, purchase ready-to-use formula in cans or disposable *Nursette®* bottles.

{affix photo here}

thoughts

What seems to be our baby's favorite toy?

_____

_____

What has made our baby express fear?

_____

_____

Who have been our baby's sitters?

_____

_____

milestones

Date

Details

Date

Details

Date

Details

Date

Details

Well-Baby Visit

Date

Length

Weight

Immunizations

Allergies or Sensitivities

Other Doctor Visits

Date

Reason

Date

Reason

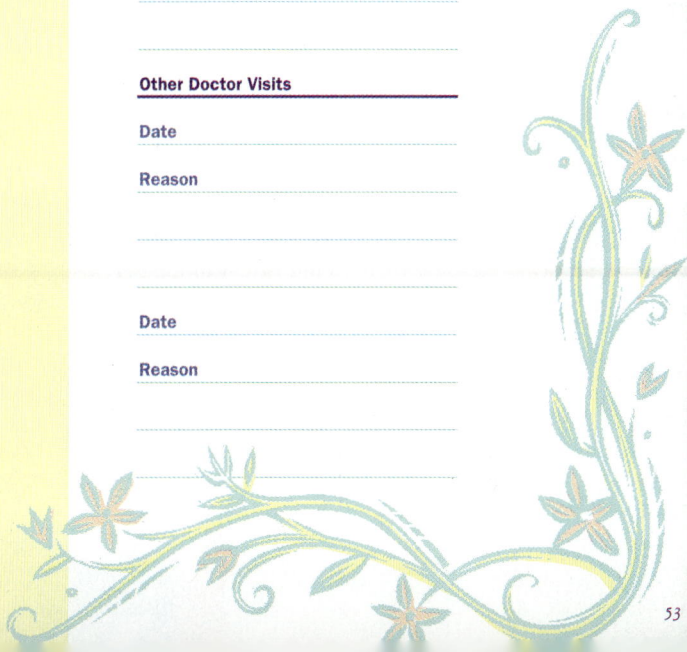

8

By the end of the eighth month, your baby may:

♥ **Show interest in peekaboo, pat-a-cake**

♥ **Show some understanding of object permanence, such as realizing a toy is present though not easily seen**

♥ **Feed self crackers or bits of finger food**

♥ **Take sips from cup**

♥ **Pull up into standing position**

♥ **Use index finger to poke at objects**

Talk to me!

By now, your baby's verbal skills are beginning to emerge. You can do much in the next few months to increase your baby's language comprehension and help him learn real, intelligible speech. Here are some suggestions:

♦ Verbally label as many objects as possible. "Look, there's a tall lady walking her big black dog."

♦ Give the baby a chance to respond. Although he's unlikely to offer his comments in identifiable English, your baby may wait for a pause in your speaking, then "say" something as a response. This teaches him about the natural give-and-take of conversation.

♦ Explain concepts. Don't just show your baby the ice cube; show him the cold ice cube and let him touch it, reinforcing the word "cold" when his fingers come into contact with the cube.

♦ Offer him the chance to follow simple directions. When feeding solid foods, ask him to give you a bite.

♦ Read! Expose your child not only to his own books, but to the sight of you reading.

Answers to Your Developmental Questions

Q: Our little girl scoots and we've seen her rock on her hands and knees, but she has no interest in crawling. What if she never crawls?
A: She probably will, but if not, it's no cause for alarm. Some babies don't crawl at all—they simply pull up to a standing position and take off on two feet.

Q: I can't keep up with my son's stacks of toys. Is there any hope?
A: Some parents cope by using laundry baskets in each room to contain the clutter at the end of the day. He might enjoy helping you put the toys away—and getting them back out again!

NUTRITION
Hold the Milk

Your baby may have grown so much during the last few months she seems big enough for cow's milk. *Resist the temptation!* Cow's milk, whether it's whole, 2 percent or skim, does not meet the nutritional needs of babies until they are at least a year old.

Cow's milk has more than twice the protein of breast milk or infant formula. This protein, which forms tough curds in a baby's stomach, is hard for babies to digest. Cow's milk also contains a type of fat that's difficult for babies to digest.

Babies need iron in their diets to prevent iron-deficiency anemia. The iron level in cow's milk is low, and difficult to absorb. There isn't enough copper, zinc or vitamin C in cow's milk, either. Plus, the sodium level is three to four times that of breast milk.

According to the American Academy of Pediatrics, iron-fortified formula is the only acceptable alternative to breast milk for the first year. That's why you should use an infant formula like *Enfamil®* if you're not breastfeeding or if you stop breastfeeding before your baby's first birthday. *Enfamil®* is patterned after breast milk to supply your baby with the right balance of nutrients.

After your baby's first birthday, you may want to consider *Next Step™* or *Next Step™ Soy* toddler formula, a transitional formula from Mead Johnson. It will provide your toddler with the iron that cow's milk lacks.

> ❀ *Make a special picture book of objects important to baby—bottle, high chair, car seat—and say the words as you point to them.*
>
> Nancy Bate, mother of two

Saying Bye-Bye to Bottles

When should a baby give up the bottle? Most doctors suggest that babies drink most of their liquids from a cup by about 1 year of age, and all liquids by 18 months. You can introduce your baby to a cup as early as 6 or 7 months of age, or when he shows interest in feeding himself. After he's used to the cup, you can substitute the cup for the bottle, one feeding at a time. Start with the midday feeding; the bottle before bedtime will probably be the last to go.

THE RIGHT START
Answers to Your Feeding Questions

Q: My daughter refuses to eat anything green. What should I do?
A: Keep at it. Many babies refuse foods simply because they are unfamiliar with them. She's still getting most of the nutrients she needs from breast milk or iron-fortified formula.

Q: I have misplaced the scoop for my baby's powdered formula. What can I use to measure?
A: To ensure accurate measurement, we recommend purchasing another can of powder to obtain a scoop.

Baby, You've Got Personality

Is your baby easygoing, shy or assertive? This lighthearted quiz may help you determine which of these broad personality types best describes your 8-month-old. Choose the answer that best describes your baby's behavior.

How does your baby let you know when he's hungry?

A. Kicks and screams and lets out loud, piercing cries.
B. Whines or cries softly.
C. Roots around, but doesn't cry unless his first signal is ignored.

Early Dental Care

Your baby's teeth are important—for proper biting and chewing as well as normal speech and appearance. To keep your baby's teeth in good shape, wipe clean with a damp gauze pad or washcloth or brush gently with an infant toothbrush moistened with water. If you prefer, you can use a special baby toothpaste. You also can protect your baby's teeth by banning the bottle at bedtime and limiting sweets as your baby grows. See page 35 for information about fluoride.

How long do your baby's meals usually last?

A. Drains bottle quickly and, when finished, pushes bottle away or clamps lips tightly.
B. Slow, steady nurser. It may take him an hour to finish his bottle.
C. Usually dozes off; nipple just slips from his lips.

When your baby is hungry, what happens if you try to distract him for a few minutes with a toy?

A. Cries until he gets his bottle.
B. Shows some momentary patience when waiting for the bottle, but does not appreciate the change in routine.
C. Is easily distracted by a toy and can wait up to 15 minutes or more.

How does your baby react when you introduce new foods?

A. Keeps lips pursed, turns head away or spits food out.
B. Sometimes turns away and often lets it dribble out of his lips.
C. Smiles and smacks lips, perhaps even strains for more.

Would you describe your baby's sleep schedule as:

A. Very irregular.
B. Somewhat regular.
C. Very predictable.

When your baby meets new people he usually:

A. Rejects them.
B. Warms up slowly, but eventually becomes comfortable.
C. Reacts with interest and enjoyment.

*If you answered **A** to most of the questions, your child may lean toward assertiveness. Assertive babies express their likes and dislikes in no uncertain terms and do not welcome changes in their routine. If most of your answers were **B**, your child may be a little shy. Shy babies typically adapt to new situations, but prefer a slow, calm, tolerant introduction and like to keep Mom or Dad near. If you answered **C** to most of the questions, chances are your baby is pretty easygoing. Easygoing babies adapt easily to change and readily accept new people and experiences.*

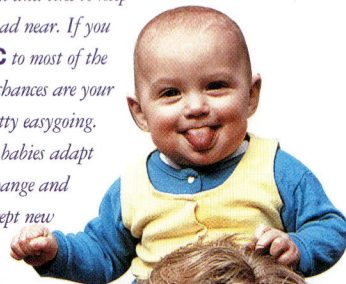

thoughts

Has our baby expressed interest in drinking from a cup?

What additional child-proofing measures have we taken during the last month?

What is the biggest change we've seen in our baby in the last month?

Does our baby seem to like music? What kind gets the biggest reaction?

In what ways have toys and baby paraphernalia taken over our household?

{affix photos here}

milestones

Date

Details

Date

Details

Date

Details

Date

Details

Well-Baby Visit

Date

Length

Weight

Immunizations

Allergies or Sensitivities

Other Doctor Visits

Date

Reason

Date

Reason

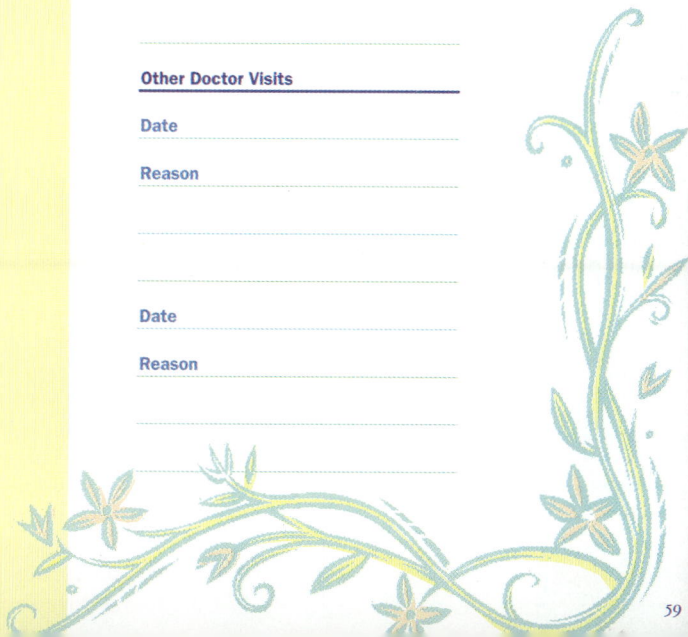

Baby's Ninth Month

Baby's Progress

By the end of the ninth month, your baby may:

♥ **Respond to own name; say "Mama" or "Dada"**

♥ **Crawl confidently, including up a stair**

♥ **Be aware of vertical space and may fear heights**

♥ **Hold objects between thumb and forefinger**

♥ **Attempt to place pegs in pegboard**

♥ **Attempt to wave bye-bye**

♥ **Play with two toys at the same time**

♥ **Exhibit some taste preferences**

Staying in Touch

The dynamics of friendship change when the demands of parenthood become a factor.

Following your baby's birth, old friendships can evolve to meet new needs, can be put on hold temporarily or can slowly die away. Truly valued friendships can flourish with a little TLC. Here are some hints to help you stay close:

➻ Don't expect your friends to be as in love with your baby as you are. Find time when you can talk without the baby being the only topic of conversation.

➻ Summer barbecues or winter potlucks are enjoyable get-togethers that aren't too taxing.

➻ Don't believe that you can have company only if the house is spotless.

"Lovies"

To you, it may look like only a blanket or a stuffed animal. To your baby, it's security. Don't worry about her attachment to her "lovie." If she's receiving ample doses of love and attention, her reliance on the lovie needn't be a concern unless it interferes with her physical and emotional development.

Answers to Your Developmental Questions

Q: Our daughter pulls up to a standing position in her crib, and we're afraid she's going to climb out. What can we do to keep her safe?

A: First, lower the crib mattress to its lowest level; that will probably take care of the problem. If not, make sure her room is child-proofed so that if she does get out of her crib, she won't face any dangers. If she does climb out, it's probably time for a child bed.

Q: We've child-proofed our house, but what about any "hidden" dangers?

A: Keep houseplants out of your baby's reach. Make sure toys have no sharp edges and all painted surfaces are lead-free. Fasten to the wall bookcase or other heavy pieces of furniture that could topple over

Forbidden Fruits

✿ *Listen to the advice and read the parenting articles—then trust your instincts on what's best for your family.*

Tracy Long, mother of one

THE RIGHT START

Answers to Your Feeding Questions

As your baby becomes more adept at eating, his menu will expand to include a variety of foods. However, certain foods should remain off-limits for some months to come. In general, restrict your baby's selection of foods to those he can mash with his gums and tongue. Stay away from foods that pose a choking hazard. They include:

• Small, hard foods such as popcorn, raisins, nuts and hard candies.

• Chunky, hard-to-chew raw vegetables, such as carrots and celery.

• Difficult-to-swallow peanut butter.

• Grapes, unless you first peel them and cut them into tiny pieces.

• Whole or sliced hot dogs, or other types of meat sticks.

• Thick-skinned fruits, such as peaches, unless you peel them first. Always remove the pit or the seeds from all fruits.

Sometimes, babies can choke on foods that seem perfectly safe. That's why you never want to let your baby eat alone. To learn what you should do in case your baby chokes, contact your local chapter of the American Red Cross.

Saying "No" to the One You Love

Hard as it is to say "no" to that adorable little baby face, even infants need to hear it sometimes. Don't think of discipline as punishment. Webster defines it as "training that develops self-control and efficiency." You want to help your baby stay out of danger and grow into someone who respects the rights of others, but you don't have to be harsh. Just say "no," then divert his attention. Be prepared to have to repeat the lesson often. Babies have short memories so be patient and be consistent.

Q: My son tries to feed himself, but the food ends up everywhere but his mouth. What should I do?
A: Relax. He will need months of practice before he becomes competent with a spoon. Give him one spoon to hold, while you feed him with another. Every few bites, dip his spoon into the food and let him guide it to his mouth. Praise his efforts and resist the impulse to take charge.

Q: I found an old can of formula at the back of my cupboard. Can I use formula that's passed its expiration date?
A: No. To ensure that your baby receives the highest nutrient value from infant formula, we recommend that you use it before the expiration date on the container.

{affix photo here}

thoughts

What differences of opinion have I encountered with the grandparents over parenting techniques?

_____

Has our baby grown attached to a special object?

_____

How am I working to keep intact my adult friendships?

_____

milestones

Date

Details

Date

Details

Date

Details

Date

Details

Well-Baby Visit

Date

Length

Weight

Immunizations

Allergies or Sensitivities

Other Doctor Visits

Date

Reason

Date

Reason

10

Baby's Progress

By the end of the tenth month, your baby may:

♥ **Stand with little support; sit from standing position**

♥ **Pretend to talk on toy telephone**

♥ **Repeat sounds and gestures for attention**

♥ **Show new fears— for example, vacuum cleaner**

♥ **Begin showing right- or left-hand dominance**

♥ **Reach behind self for toy without having to look for it**

♥ **Point to body parts**

Drs. DOS and Mac

Instead of flipping through home medical books, you now can flip on your computer switch for a quick home remedy. With a CD-ROM and one of these multimedia software packages, you can select from a symptoms checklist and receive advice for non-threatening maladies. (Of course, when in doubt, call the doctor.) Some of these packages include:

🐦 **THE DOCTOR'S BOOK OF HOME REMEDIES** (Compton's New Media; retail $39.95). Published by the editors of *Prevention Magazine*.

🐦 **MAYO CLINIC FAMILY HEALTH BOOK** (IVI Publishing; retail $59.99). An interactive guide to human anatomy, first aid, fitness, diseases and disorders.

🐦 **THE FAMILY DOCTOR,** 3rd Edition (Creative Multimedia; retail $79.99). Question and answer section; more than 2,300 commonly asked health questions.

🐦 **DR. SCHUELER'S HOME MEDICAL ADVISOR PRO** (Pixel Perfect; retail $99.95). A huge data base of symptoms and illnesses, prescription drugs and medical tests.

A New Perspective

For many, having a baby makes them appreciate their own parents even more. Recording those insights could make a wonderful Mother's Day or Father's Day gift for grandparents. One young mother touched her father's heartstrings when she wrote: "When my baby is older, I will climb the trees with her. I will take her to the beach and let her bury me with sand up to my neck. And I will teach her to play softball and checkers and chess; because, Daddy, as a parent, I want to be just like you."

Answers to Your Developmental Questions

Q: Our daughter seems to have developed a nagging cough, but our pediatrician can't find anything wrong. We're concerned.

A: If medical problems have been ruled out, your daughter probably has discovered that her coughing is a neat sound that makes the adults come running. Other children may yell repeatedly, or bang a toy or make spitting noises. Chances are the cough will disappear if you and your husband downplay its importance.

NUTRITION
The Finicky Eater

Although he's not even a year old, your baby has developed some definite opinions about food—and they don't always agree with yours. The older your baby gets, the more challenging mealtimes may become. Here are some tips to help make mealtime a happy time.

Remember that your baby's appetite is irregular at this age; he's not growing as fast as he was a few months ago. He may play with his food at breakfast, turn up his nose at lunch, then eat ravenously at dinner. The next day he might turn this pattern around. Despite this erratic behavior, your baby usually

Fat Facts

What's good for grownups isn't necessarily good for babies, especially when it comes to fat. For the first two years, your baby's need for fat is much higher than an adult's. That's because fat plays a vital role in the development of your baby's eyes, brain and nervous system. It also provides your baby with essential fat-soluble vitamins and acts as a concentrated energy source.

❊ *Use ice cube trays to freeze baby-sized portions of chopped meat and vegetables. Reheat a cube in the microwave for a quick entrée.*

David Walsh, mother of one

knows how much food he needs. Resist the urge to nag, bribe or force your baby to eat. Never insist that a child clean his plate. Let your baby decide when he's full.

Although you can't control the quantity of food your baby eats, you can certainly control the quality. Concentrate on serving your baby a variety of healthful foods, even if he continues to reject them. Gradually, he may learn to like them.

Whatever you do, try to stay calm. Breast milk or iron-fortified formula is still your baby's main source of nutrition.

Answers to Your Feeding Questions

Q: When our son joins us at the table, he tries to grab our food. What kinds of table foods can he eat?
A: He can probably manage pieces of peeled, soft fruit such as bananas. Mash cooked vegetables for him; give him bagels or crackers to chew on. Finely chop a small portion of lean meat or chicken.

Q: I have recently switched my baby formula from concentrated liquid to powdered. When I mix the powder, it appears lighter than the liquid. Why?
A: Formula prepared from powder will be lighter in color and thinner in consistency than concentrated liquid or ready-to-use formula due to differences between the liquid and powder manufacturing processes.

Fire Drill

In case of fire, here's information to help you get you and your baby out of the house safely:
•Have frequent fire drills using alternate escape routes. •Practice checking doors for heat, staying low in case of smoke, not stopping for possessions, and meeting in the same place outside each time.
•Get a red-dot window sticker from your local fire department and place it in baby's bedroom window, so it can be easily spotted by firefighters who come to the rescue.

What to Tell the Babysitter

Relax and enjoy your night out—resting assured your babysitter has adequate information to handle any problem that might arise. Some information to be sure to pass on:

- Your family members' first and last names, home address and phone number.
- Telephone numbers for ambulance, police and fire department.
- Telephone number for the poison-control center.
- Name and number(s) where you can be reached.
- Baby's schedule: approximate time of next bottle, bedtime, notes on typical routine.
- Time you're expected to arrive home.

And before you walk out the door, did you:

- Show the sitter where bottles are kept and how to warm them?
- Offer ways to comfort your baby if he or she becomes frightened or upset?
- Suggest what to do if your child has trouble going to sleep or wakes up during the night?
- Provide the location of first-aid supplies?
- Demonstrate how locks on doors and baby gates operate?
- Suggest how to answer the telephone, and when and if to answer the doorbell?

Get a handle on your baby's routine at your caregiver's home or facility. Regularly spend a lunch—and sometimes a morning—with your baby, so you'll be able to see how her weekday routine differs from her weekend one. Drop in unexpectedly to see what's happening. See how much time caregivers are spending talking and playing with *each* child. Spending this time with your child will not only let your caregiver know you're tuned into your child's quality of care—it will let your baby know, too.

What's That Song?

Creative expression through music takes training, but the ability to appreciate creative music comes quite naturally. You can help instill a love of music in your baby.
■ Make music a part of your daily lives and your family's time together.
■ Play and sing songs that encourage participation, such as "Old MacDonald."
■ Consider baby-safe tape players, music boxes and toy instruments. A harmonica inspires great experiments in sound.

thoughts

What is our baby's favorite food?

Has our baby rejected any foods?

Is our baby standing, walking or nearly walking?

What has been the biggest surprise about our baby this month?

What is the biggest change I've seen in our baby during the last month?

{affix photos here}

milestones

Date

Details

Date

Details

Date

Details

Date

Details

Well-Baby Visit

Date

Length

Weight

Immunizations

Allergies or Sensitivities

Other Doctor Visits

Date

Reason

Date

Reason

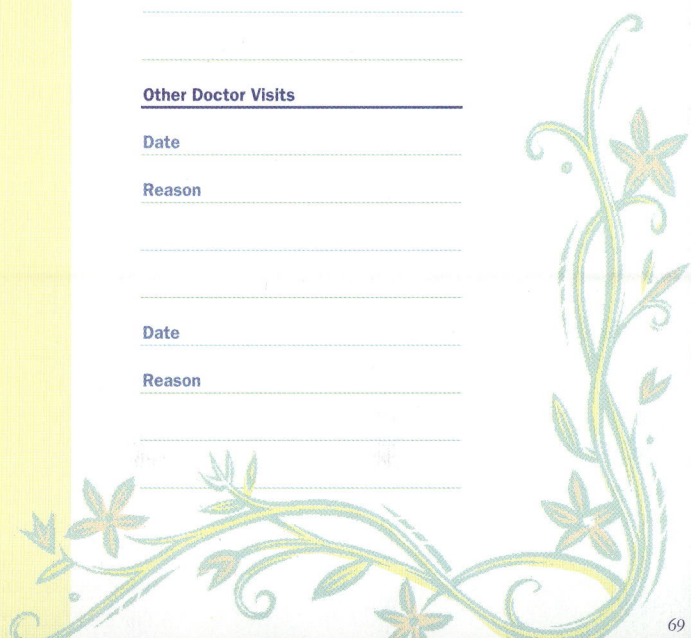

Baby's Progress

By the end of the eleventh month, your baby may:

♥ **Begin walking while holding on to furniture for support; take one step without holding on to supporting object**

♥ **Make long, babbling sentences, complete with vocal inflection; say one word clearly other than "Mama" or "Dada"**

♥ **Hold out arm or leg to aid in dressing**

♥ **Drop objects for someone to pick up**

♥ **Drink from cup with sipper lid**

♥ **Understand simple commands, such as "Bring me the ball" or "Pat the puppy"**

Baby Goes to Market

Squirming. Climbing. Boxed energy. If any of those words describe your baby, here are some tips for roping in the wiggle worm while you're shopping:

✳ Some stores have carts with safety belts in them. Or you can purchase a commercially available harness made for strollers.

✳ Keep breakables out of the baby's reach. One mom relates having a full basket of groceries ruined when her baby boy grabbed the car-

ton of eggs she had placed right on top.

✳ Most importantly, keep one hand and one eye on the cart all the time. Kidnappers can snatch a baby faster than you can say, "Whoops, I forgot the mustard."

To Each His or Her Own

"Sugar and spice and everything nice" and "Snips and snails and puppy-dog tails." What are the real behavioral differences between little girls and boys?

● **On the average, baby girls tend to be more sensitive to touch than boys, and they smile and frown more.**

● **Boys a few hours old usually are stronger and more active.**

● **By preschool age, girls tend to be better at skills requiring balance and body control, such as hopping and skipping.**

● **Preschool-age boys generally are better at throwing, catching and kicking—tasks that demand strength and speed.**

Answers to Your Developmental Questions

Q: Now that our daughter is walking around furniture and taking steps on her own, should we buy her special shoes?

A: In recent years, doctors have discovered that the best shoes are no shoes at all. The feet, like the hands, develop better when left uncovered; walking barefoot helps build the arches and strengthen the ankles and lower legs.

Q: Our daughter throws a tantrum every time we place her in her car seat. We can't stand the screams; should we take her out?

A: First, although it's admittedly difficult to endure screaming, never allow your daughter to ride outside her seat. In addition to being unsafe, letting your daughter out of the seat teaches her that she'll get her way if she screams long enough.

NUTRITION: *A Place at the Table*

❀ Oat ring cereal mixed with yogurt makes a tasty—albeit messy—treat that baby can feed herself.

Barb Ruble, mother of three

Now that you've introduced your baby to table foods, you may want to start including him at the dinner table, too. If you're like most parents, however, you'll want to work your baby into family meals gradually. Feeding a baby at this age usually is a slow, and always a messy, process.

To ease the transition, feed your baby most of his meal before you seat the rest of the family. Then you can let your baby munch on finger foods while the rest of the family enjoys their meal. Try to be flexible. Getting everyone in the house on the same schedule may require some adjustments.

If your baby hasn't yet established a three-meals-a-day routine, this would be a good time to encourage him to do so. As you modify his schedule, it's important to keep the breast milk or iron-fortified formula coming—at mealtime, snacktime and bedtime. Your baby still depends on the nutrition it provides.

When you feed your baby—with or without the rest of the family—continue to encourage him to use a spoon; offer him liquids in a cup. At this age, your baby's attempts at self-feeding may result in more food on the high-chair tray and the floor than in his mouth, but that's all part of the learning process.

Family Far Away

It's tough having a baby when your extended family is miles away. But it's possible to establish a network of supporters who can become your surrogate family. Reach out to other families in your neighborhood, your church, synagogue or your daycare. Many parents join support groups or other types of family-oriented community groups. Bonds grow out of sharing mutual interests. Also, by volunteering your services to help others, you can become a valued member of a group and be more likely to find help from others when you are in need.

Answers to Your Feeding Questions

Q: My baby is losing interest in breast-feeding and I plan to wean. Should I give him a bottle or a cup?
A: If your baby is comfortable using a cup, by all means bypass the bottle. Whether you give your baby a cup or a bottle, make sure you feed him iron-fortified formula until his first birthday.

Q: Can I recycle our formula cans?
A: Mead Johnson shares your concern for the environment. Our cans are steel, and technically are recyclable. However, many recycling centers accept only aluminum cans. We suggest calling your local facility to determine whether it accepts steel cans.

{affix photo here}

thoughts

Who has proved to be an invaluable family resource the last few months?

_____

_____

How would I describe our baby's personality?

_____

_____

What's it been like taking our baby to the grocery store?

_____

_____

milestones

Date

Details

Date

Details

Date

Details

Date

Details

Well-Baby Visit

Date

Length

Weight

Immunizations

Allergies or Sensitivities

Other Doctor Visits

Date

Reason

Date

Reason

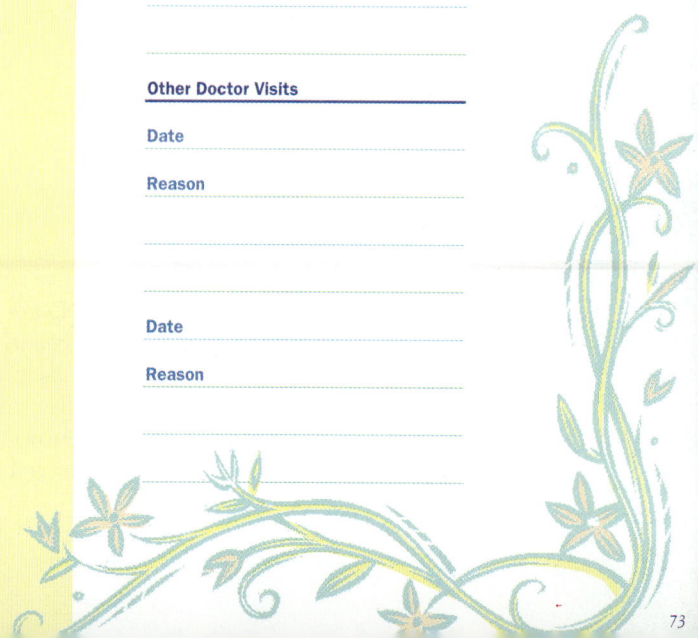

12

Baby's Progress

By the end of the twelfth month, your baby may:

♥ **Walk with or without assistance**

♥ **Erupt a first set of molars**

♥ **Give a kiss on request**

♥ **Point to desired object**

♥ **Enjoy applause for new abilities**

♥ **Scribble with a chunky crayon if paper is taped to work surface**

♥ **Enjoy push-and-pull toys**

PREPARING FOR ANOTHER PREGNANCY

You have one child barely on table food and you're expecting another. Stay calm. You'll handle it beautifully, and so will your first-born with a little planning.

• Don't try to prepare a toddler too soon for the new baby. With such a hazy concept of time, the child will be confused by the wait.

• A few weeks before the birth, begin talking about the new baby. Emphasize what fun it will be to be an older brother or sister.

• Do any rearranging months in advance, so the toddler won't feel pushed out.

• To diminish fears, prepare the child for the fact that you'll be away for a few days, while you are at the hospital.

It's Never Too Soon *to Save for College*

Your baby hasn't even enrolled in preschool yet. Is it too soon to start saving for college? Financial planners agree: "No!"

Some financial forecasters predict tuition costs will triple in the next 18 years. The sooner you begin preparing, the better. Shop for investments that provide strong long-term results:

$ Owning a home is a good investment that carries tax benefits.

$ Employer retirement savings plans such as 401(k)'s reduce your taxable income and usually perform well. You typically can borrow against this money for college expenses.

$ For long-term investing, most financial advisers suggest a combination of mutual funds and savings bonds, such as Series EE bonds.

$ Get reliable advice from reputable financial advisers before taking financial risks.

$ Don't make the mistake of counting on low-interest student loans. Investing today will earn money; borrowing tomorrow will cost you money.

NUTRITION
Now, Brown Cow?

Sometime around your baby's first birthday, you can introduce him to cow's milk. But first, you'll want to make sure he's ready. Because your baby no longer will be receiving the extra nutrients that breast milk or formula provides, he should be eating regular meals that include a variety of foods.

Before making the switch from breast milk or formula to cow's milk, get an OK from your baby's doctor. Most doctors recommend feeding babies whole milk until the age of 2 to ensure an adequate supply of fat. Babies need sufficient levels of fat in their diets to ensure optimal development of their eyes, brains and nervous systems. Never give a 1-year-old baby skim milk; the protein and sodium levels are just too high. The cow's milk you feed your baby should always be pasteurized.

As an alternative to cow's milk, your doctor may recommend *Next Step*™ or *Next Step*™ *Soy* toddler formula, an easily digested, balanced formula for babies who've reached their first birthday. *Next Step*™ is fortified with iron, which cow's milk lacks.

Child's Menu, Please

Your baby sincerely wants to make you happy, but that doesn't always assure good behavior in public. Here are some tips for keeping your sanity when eating out.
- Take along some cereal or crackers to tide over your child while you are waiting to be served.
- Take along a cup that baby can drink from easily.
- Try to order in advance for faster service. Or go to cafeteria-style or fast-food restaurants where you can eat right away.
- Take along a few quiet toys for after-dinner entertainment.
- Don't let baby wander around. Some diners may be entertained by cuteness, but many won't appreciate the interruption.
- It's hard for most children to sit quietly for long. If restless fussing becomes a problem, don't discipline at the table. Instead, take the baby for a short, diversionary walk.

THE RIGHT START

Answers to Your Feeding Questions

Q: My baby is really attached to his bottle. How can I help him give it up?

A: Some experts recommend weaning soon after the first birthday, before an even stronger attachment to the bottle forms. If your baby isn't ready to give up his bottle, try imposing a few rules. Limit the number of bottles he receives each day to two or three, supplementing with snacks and drinks from a cup. Give all bottle feedings on your lap—don't allow your baby to walk around the house or go to bed with his bottle.

Answers to Your Developmental Questions

Q: My mother insists that I was toilet-trained by my first birthday. I can't imagine starting to train my daughter. Isn't 12 months just too early?

A: Yes. In your mother's day, parents did little more than predict when the baby would pass urine or have a bowel movement, then "catch" the waste in the toilet. Most babies don't show signs of interest until close to the second birthday.

Q: Our son seems to understand, but ignore, the word "no." Is he too young to be disciplined?

A: No, as he must learn to live safely in the world. Child-care experts suggest using "time-out" to remove a child from a dangerous or overstimulating situation.

Twelfth Month:
Toddling Along

CONGRATULATIONS! You and your baby have made it to 1 year. And what a wonderful, wild ride it's been. The first year is amazing in terms of baby's growth and development, but there are many milestones to look forward to. Welcome to toddlerhood; here's a preview.

By the end of the 15th month, your child may:
• Climb up stairs on hands and knees
• Throw a ball, extending the arm at the elbow joint
• Try to turn a doorknob
• Have a speaking vocabulary of at least four to six words
• Recognize the names of the major body parts

By the end of the 18th month, your child may:
• Jump off the floor with both feet
• Turn pages of a book, two or three at a time
• Build a tower of three or four blocks
• Have a speaking vocabulary of about 10 words
• Enjoy such songs as "Old MacDonald"

By the end of the 21st month, your child may:
• Walk up stairs, holding rail, with both feet on one step
• Kick a large ball in forward direction
• Be able to fold a piece of paper once
• Build a tower of five or six blocks
• Have a speaking vocabulary of 20 or more words
• Join two words to form a sentence

By the end of the 24th month, your child may:
• Be able to run, but not to start quickly or stop well
• Go up and down stairs alone, not alternating feet
• Turn pages of a book, one at a time
• Have fully developed right-handedness or left-handedness
• Have a speaking vocabulary of 50 or more words
• Be able to recite his first and last names

thoughts

What plans do we have for celebrating our baby's first birthday?

What words can our baby say?

What makes our baby laugh?

What is the biggest change I've seen in our baby during the last month?

How have my spouse and I changed over the past year?

{affix photos here}

milestones

Date

Details

Date

Details

Date

Details

Date

Details

Well-Baby Visit

Date

Length

Weight

Immunizations

Allergies or Sensitivities

Other Doctor Visits

Date

Reason

Date

Reason

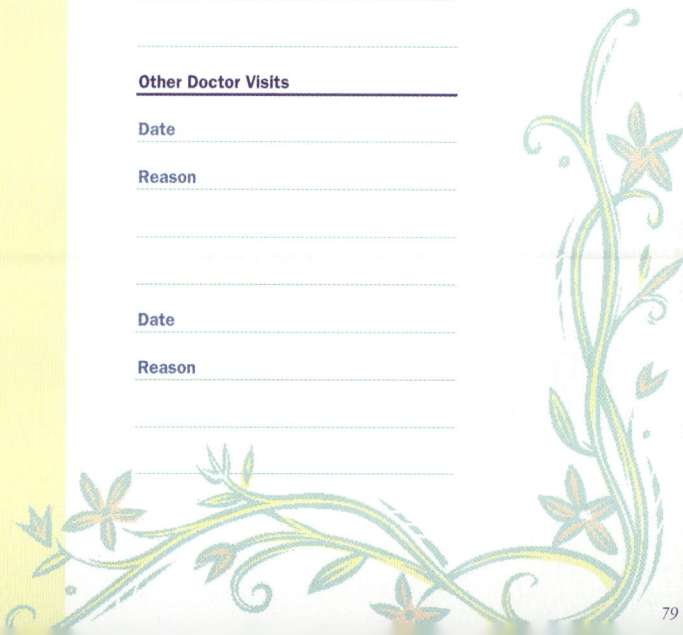

index